PHYSICS

For Advanced Level

Jim Breithaupt

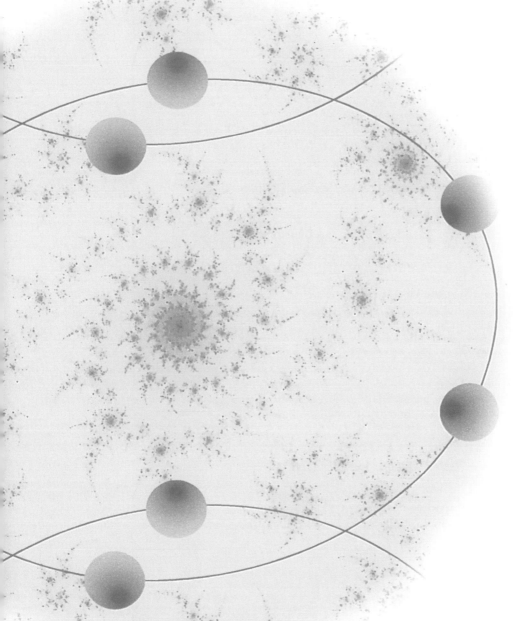

Stanley Thornes Publishers Ltd

Course Study Gui

First published in 2000 by:

Stanley Thornes (Publishers) Ltd
Ellenborough House
Wellington Street
Cheltenham
GL50 1YW

00 01 02 03 04 / 10 9 8 7 6 5 4 3 2 1

A catalogue record of this book is available from the British Library.

ISBN 0 7487 4315 4

New Understanding Physics for Advanced Level
ISBN 0 7487 4314 6

New Understanding Physics for Advanced Level plus Course Study Guide
ISBN 0 7487 4416 2

New Understanding Physics for Advanced Level plus Course Study Guide (Trade Edition)
ISBN 0 7487 4466 5

Solutions of Physics for Advanced Level CD-ROM
Single- and Multi-user Versions available
Free sample available on request
Please contact the publisher at the address given above
or telephone Customer Services on 01242 267273

Acknowledgements
The Publishers are grateful to Patrick McNeill for checking the accuracy of the information about Advanced level and key skills qualifications.

The Publishers thank Martyn Chillmaid for permission to reproduce the photograph on p.6

Typeset by Mathematical Composition Setters Ltd, Salisbury, Wiltshire.
Printed in Great Britain by Ashford Colour Press, Gosport, Hampshire.

Contents

Awarding Bodies

The Associated Examining Board (AEB):

AQA (AEB), Stag Hill House, Guildford, Surrey
GU2 5XJ
Website: www.aeb.org.uk
e-mail: aeb@aeb.org.uk

Edexcel:

Excel Foundation,
Stewart House, 32 Russell Square,
London WC1B 5DN
Website: www.edexcel.org.uk
e-mail: enquiries@edexcel.org.uk

Northern Examinations and Assessment Board (NEAB):

AQA (NEAB), Devas Street, Manchester M15 6EX
Website: www.neab.ac.uk/syllabus/maths/
physics.htm
e-mail: physics@neab.ac.uk

Northern Ireland Council for the Curriculum Examinations and Assessment (CCEA):

CCEA, Clarendon Dock, 29 Clarendon Road,
Belfast BT1 3BG
Website: www.ccea.org.uk
e-mail: info@ccea.org.uk

For Oxford, Cambridge and Oxford & Cambridge examinations see:

OCR, Publications Department,
Mill Wharf, Mill Street, Birmingham B6 4BU
Website: www.ocr.org.uk

Welsh Joint Education Committee (WJEC):

Welsh Joint Education Committee, 245 Eastern
Avenue, Cardiff CF5 2YX
Website (English language): www.wjec.co.uk
        (Welsh language): www.cbac.co.uk
e-mail: bookshop@wjec.co.uk

1 Moving on from GCSE

This Course Study Guide is designed to help you to bridge the gap from physics at GCSE to AS and Advanced level. The guide is presented as a separate book rather than part of the main textbook *New Understanding Physics for Advanced Level (4th Edition)*. It provides support material on important skills in physics and also provides essential bridging material from GCSE to AS and A-level, without making the main text book too large. In addition, it provides important guidance for revision and examination skills.

The differences between studying GCSE and Advanced level Physics

Successful completion of a GCSE Physics or balanced science course is an essential requirement for AS and A-level Physics. Every Advanced level course is now organized as a three-module 1st year course called Advanced Subsidiary (AS) level, followed by a three-module 2nd year course referred to as the A2 course. Each subject can therefore be studied to AS level (in one year) or to Advanced level (usually in two years including the AS year). The grade awarded at Advanced level is based on A2 **and** AS marks. You can't afford to take things easy at the start of the AS level course; it's all too easy to fall into the trap of thinking that the examination is years away and so there's plenty of time. There isn't! An AS or Advanced level course is really a sequence of stages. All tests, apart from coursework, can be taken at the end of the course, but most students will take some tests before the end, maybe as early as the start of the second term in the AS year. By the end of your first term, you should have completed over one third of the AS course, so you can't afford to waste time at any stage, especially at the start. You need to keep up with your studies throughout the course. Fall behind and you soon find the work piles up. With several subjects to study for, you've got your work cut out.

What are the essentials for success at AS and A-level?

- Mathematics is an important feature of AS and A-level Physics. You need to be competent at basic arithmetic, algebra and graph work. Chapter 4 should be helpful in this respect. If you are not studying AS or A-level Mathematics, you will need to work that much harder than your 'mathematical' colleagues.
- Understanding key ideas and being able to link them together is an important part of AS and A-level Physics. Your previous course in physics has lots of facts and formulae; AS and A-level have even more and you must try to understand the principles behind the formulae for example.

- Initiative on your part is essential. There is a much greater emphasis on individuality than in your previous course. You should be prepared to question ideas that are new to you. Teaching methods differ from GCSE and you have to organise your own notes. Great emphasis is placed on problem solving and on laboratory skills. Your teacher/lecturer is not there just to transmit knowledge, etc., but is your adviser and guide. Make use of the resources available to you, not just in the laboratory or the library, but also any video or computer programs.
- Organising your studies yourself around your timetable is necessary otherwise you will struggle. With, say, four or five AS levels and possibly some other studies on your timetable in year 1 followed by at least three A2 courses in year 2, you need to plan in advance to ensure work is handed in on time. The ability to organise your private study time is as important as the content of your course. At university, the ability is taken for granted. If you go to university and can't organise yourself, you won't survive the first year, so you must learn to organise yourself at AS and A-level. Draw up a timetable for your private study time and allocate equal time, say, about six hours per week, to each subject. Of course, as you approach examinations and tests, you need to spend extra time on private study – your social life suffers at such times! However, if you plan and work to a schedule, you should be able to fit in a social life. With an organised schedule, it is easier to cope with the inevitable emergencies such as missing classes through illness.

AS and A-level Physics specifications vary slightly between awarding bodies. All courses have a core of topics that are covered in *New Understanding Physics for Advanced Level (4th edition)*. Each course has its own features built around the core topics so you should obtain a copy of your examination specifications to guide your revision. All AS and A-level courses place great emphasis on understanding key concepts which you must be able to explain and to use. Most courses build on basic principles from previous studies, so a thorough understanding of these principles is essential. Check your previous course notes when you come to each topic at AS and A-level and identify points that you found difficult; working at these points should help your progress in the topic at AS and A-level. Try past questions from recent GCSE papers to build up your confidence. The emphasis on understanding ideas at AS and A-level is reflected in the way most courses are organised.

Use of *New Understanding Physics* and this *Course Study Guide* will depend on you, your teacher and your subject specification, of course. The book is designed to cover the core topics of all AS and A-level Physics specifications with the emphasis on explaining difficult ideas. The book attempts to follow the requirements in its organisation, but you ought not to expect to progress through your course simply from Section A to Section B to Section C and so on. You may, for example, find that you start your course with the study of wave motion, then you move on to d.c. electricity and electronics, and then to materials.

Your teacher controls the sequence of the course, and *New Understanding Physics* and this *Course Study Guide* are not organised for any particular sequence. You may or may not use the books a lot in class, depending on your teacher. You will certainly need to use the book to reinforce your studies. For example, if you are uncertain about a topic you have covered in class, you can use the book to read up at home on that topic.

Occasionally, you may need to refer to a library book, especially if you are investigating or researching a project. To help you to check your grasp of the topics in each section, there is a selection of short questions at the end of each chapter.

Making and using notes is a skill you need to develop. At first you may need to rewrite your notes to make them useful for revision. With practice, you ought to become capable of making notes in class that do not need rewriting afterwards – although you do need to check them. Add to your notes by reading your textbooks. Many students keep their main file of notes at home and take a separate file with only the current topic to and from classes. This has two chief advantages: you carry less weight round in your bag, and your main notes are secure at home. If you lose your complete set of notes a month before the examination, then you will need to spend valuable time and energy catching up in a hurry! As each topic is completed, you can file it at home – after checking you understand the topic.

Your notes are for you to use; keep them well-organised in your file, highlight key points and equations, use clear, numbered headings, and make topic charts linking the key aspects of each topic (see Fig 1.1).

Now let's consider the essentials of how you can get to grips with physics. Your studies in class ought to include plenty of practical work and you should see plenty of demonstrations in the 'chalk and talk' sessions. If you are not given notes, you need to make your own. You may be asked to work through a series of problems, written or practical.

The idea is to develop your understanding of a concept or to further your skill in a particular area. Be prepared to ask if you do not understand. Physics is a 'linear' subject and you build on one

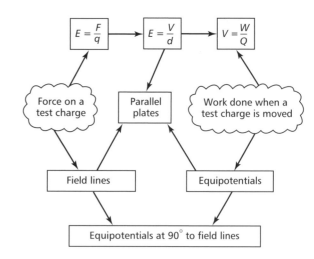

Fig 1.1 Linking a topic

topic to understand others. If you don't understand some basic point, then you may find it holds up your progress in a later topic. That's why it is important to use your notes and textbooks to ensure you have grasped each topic as it is taught.

Understanding physics is achieved by different routes for different people. All routes require a body of facts to work on. Memorise basic facts and formulae as you meet them in your course so that you can think about how they fit together – without continually having to check the facts against your notes. For example, suppose you are attempting to grasp the essential ideas in the topic 'Uniform electric fields' you could ask:

- What is a line of force?
- What is the definition of electric field strength?
- What is the pattern of the lines of force in a uniform field?
- Does the force on a test charge vary with position in a uniform field?

The answers to the questions are some of the key facts for uniform electric fields. You must be able to remember the key facts and link them together. A 'spider diagram' is a useful aid to see and remember how key facts and ideas are linked together.

Check your ability to recall key facts and ideas by testing yourself regularly. Write down the basic facts from memory and check them against your notes. Check at regular intervals to ensure you can remember key facts and ideas and the links between them. Reread your notes on the topic regularly once you have grasped the topic. After a while, you ought to find that the ideas become second nature and can be recalled with little effort.

If you think you have mastered a topic, ask yourself these general questions.

- Can you solve problems on the topic? Short questions can test your recall of facts and your understanding of the topic. Longer questions can test your understanding of links between topics as well as within a given topic.

- Can you explain the topic to a classmate? Imagine you are writing an account of the topic for a classmate who has been absent. See what you can produce, then check it against your notes.
- Can you apply the topic to unusual situations? Try questions on the topic that involve unusual applications (i.e. ones you have not met before). Such questions test your understanding of the basic principles by asking you to apply basic principles to an unusual situation.
- Can you understand these basic principles as applied to the experiments and demonstrations that you have seen? Could you explain each experiment, principle, etc. to that classmate who keeps missing classes?

Practical work is an integral part of AS and Advanced level Physics and you have to learn to use equipment such as oscilloscopes, multimeters, spectrometers, travelling microscopes, micrometers and so on. You ought to find Chapter 6 in this *Course Study Guide* helpful for developing laboratory skills as you work through the experiments one by one. Microcomputers are used to simulate experiments, and computer programs can be useful for revision or for situations beyond normal resources (e.g. nuclear reactor simulation). Microcomputers in the physics laboratory can be 'interfaced' to equipment for making measurements. Such a system can usually be programmed to measure several different physical quantities over the same period, and the program can be written to include data analysis routines.

Microcomputer programs to illustrate difficult ideas and concepts are helpful. For example, you may have seen a program that simulates radioactive decay.

When the program runs, a grid of boxes appears on the screen with each box filled by a solid circle, ●. Each solid circle represents a radioactive nucleus that disintegrates to form a stable nucleus. When this happens, the solid circle becomes an open circle, ○. The program is written so that the solid circles change at random to open circles. A graph on the screen shows how the number of radioactive atoms remaining changes with time.

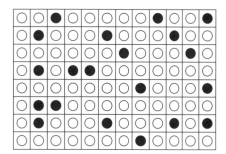

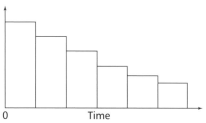

Fig 1.2 Radioactivity program

2 | Techniques in Advanced level physics

Before you move on to study physics at advanced level, this book provides the opportunity to brush up and reinforce knowledge and skills from GCSE that you will meet from the outset of your AS level Physics course. Questions and answers are provided at intervals so you can check your progress. Tests are also provided at intervals so you can make sure you have mastered all the skills in this section by checking your answers against the correct answers at the foot of the page. The skills in this chapter are developed further in chapters 4 to 7 of the *Course Study Guide* and you should make use of these chapters as you progress through the course.

 ## Handling numbers and units

Whenever you make a record of a measurement, you must always note the correct unit as well as the numerical value of the measurement.

Scientific units

Scientists use a single system of units to avoid unnecessary effort and time converting between different units of the same quantity. This system, the **Système International** (or SI system), is based on a defined unit for each of five physical quantities, as listed in Table 2.1. The symbol for each unit is also given in the Table. You will find the exact definition of each of these units on p 37. Units of all other quantities are derived from these five SI base units.

Physical quantity	Unit
Mass	kilogram (kg)
Length	metre (m)
Time	second (s)
Electric current	ampere (A)
Temperature	kelvin (K)

Table 2.1 SI base units

Derived units

The following examples show how the units of all other physical quantities are derived from the base units.

- The unit of area is the square metre, abbreviated to m^2.
- The unit of volume is the cubic metre, abbreviated to m^3.
- The unit of density, which is defined as mass per unit volume, is the kilogram per cubic metre,

abbreviated to $kg\,m^{-3}$. The negative sign in a unit means 'per' (e.g. per m^3).
- The unit of speed is the metre per second, abbreviated to $m\,s^{-1}$.

nano-	micro-	milli-	kilo-	mega-	giga-
10^{-9}	10^{-6}	10^{-3}	10^{3}	10^{6}	10^{9}
(n)	(μ)	(m)	(k)	(M)	(G)

Table 2.2 Numerical prefixes

Note: the cubic centimetre (cm^3) and the gram (g) are in common use and are therefore allowed as exceptions to the above system of prefixes.

Numerical prefixes

These are used to avoid unwieldy numerical values. The most common numerical prefixes are shown in Table 2.2.

Numbers in standard form

Numerical values smaller than 0.001 and greater than 1000 are usually expressed in **standard form** for convenience. The numerical value is written as a number between 1 and 10 multiplied by an appropriate power of ten corresponding to how many places and the direction the decimal point is moved until the number is between 1 and 10.

If the number is greater than 10, the decimal point must be moved to the left. This is shown as a positive power of ten (e.g. 10^3 for 1000).

If the number is smaller than 1, the decimal point must be moved to the right. This is shown as a negative power of ten (e.g. 10^{-2} for 0.01).

EXAMPLES

a The mean radius of the Earth is 6 360 000 m. The decimal point after the final zero needs to be moved six places leftwards to arrive at 6.36. Therefore, in standard form, the Earth's radius is 6.36×10^6 m.

b The speed of light in free space is 300 000 000 $m\,s^{-1}$. This is written as $3.0 \times 10^8\ m\,s^{-1}$ in standard form.

c The wavelength of yellow light from a sodium lamp is 0.000 000 59 m or 5.9×10^{-7} m in standard form.

Note the negative power of ten because the decimal point is moved rightwards to arrive at 5.9.

> *Reminder*
> *Mass   1000 g = 1 kg*
> *Length   1000 mm = 100 cm = 1 m*
> *Area $10^6\ mm^2 = 10^4\ cm^2 = 1\ m^2$*
> *Volume $10^9\ mm^3 = 10^6\ cm^3 = 1\ m^3$*

Using a calculator

As you progress through your Advanced level course, you should become increasingly adept at using a scientific calculator. At this stage, you should be able to use a calculator to add, subtract, multiply, divide, find squares and square roots, and calculate sines, cosines and tangents of angles. In addition, you need to know the following operations:

How to display and read the powers of ten of a numerical value from a calculator

To key in a number in standard form (e.g. 3.0×10^8), follow these steps.

__STEP 1__ Key in the number between 1 and 10 (e.g. 3.0).

__STEP 2__ Press the button marked EE.

__STEP 3__ Key in the power of ten (e.g. 8).

The display will now read '3.0   08' which should be read as 3.0×10^8 (not 3.0^8 which means 3.0 times itself eight times).

If the power of ten is a negative number (e.g. 10^{-8} not 10^8), press the button marked '+/−' after step 3 to change the sign on the power.

WORKED EXAMPLE

Light travels a distance of 1.5×10^4 m in 5.0×10^{-5} s. Use this data and the equation 'speed = distance/time' to show that the speed of light is 3.0×10^8 m s^{-1}.

Solution
__STEP 1__ Key in 1.5×10^4 as explained above
__STEP 2__ Press the ÷ button
__STEP 3__ Key in 5.0×10^{-5} as explained above.
__STEP 4__ The display should show '3.0   8'. The answer is 3.0×10^8 m s^{-1}

How to raise a number to a given power (e.g. 2.1^3)

__STEP 1__ Key in the number (e.g. 2.1).
__STEP 2__ Press the button y^x.
__STEP 3__ Key in the power (e.g. 3) and press ' = '.

The display will now read the number raised to the power.

If the power is a fraction (1/2 for a square root or 1/3 for a cubed root), key in the power in step 3 in parentheses (brackets).

WORKED EXAMPLE

Calculate the cube root of 2.9×10^6.

Solution
__STEP 1__ Key in 2.9×10^6 as explained earlier.
__STEP 2__ Press the button 'y^x'.
__STEP 3__ Key in '$(1 \div 3)$'.
__STEP 4__ Press = .

The display should show '1.426   02' so the answer is 142.6.

 ## Questions (see below for answers)

1. Copy and complete the following conversions.
   a) (i) 500 mm = ___ m   (ii) 3.2 m = ___ cm
      (iii) 9560 cm = ___ m
   b) (i) 0.45 kg = ___ g (ii) 1997 g = ___ kg
      (iii) 54 000 kg = ___ $\times 10^7$ g
2. Write the following values in standard form.
   a) 150 million kilometres in metres
   b) 365 days in seconds
   c) 630 nanometres in metres
   d) 25.7 micrograms in kilograms
   e) 150 metres in millimetres
   f) 1.245 micrometres in metres
3. Use the equation 'average speed = distance/time' to calculate the average speed in m s^{-1} of:
   a) a vehicle that travels a distance of 9000 m in a time of 450 s,
   b) a vehicle that travels a distance of 144 km in 2 hours,
   c) a particle that travels a distance of 0.30 nm in a time of 2.0×10^{-18} s.
4. Calculate each of the following.
   a) 6.7^3 b) $(4.2 \times 10^8)^{1/2}$ c) $(3.8 \times 10^{-5})^{1/4}$

Using symbols and equations in physics

Physical quantities are usually represented by a standard symbol. For example, time is represented by the symbol t. Greek symbols are sometimes used (e.g. the Greek letter ρ (pronounced rho) is used for density). The symbol represents a numerical value **and its unit**.

Equations and formulae in physics are usually presented in symbolic form. For example, the word equation, density $= \dfrac{\text{mass}}{\text{volume}}$ can be written $\rho = \dfrac{m}{V}$.

Note that the SI unit of density is the kilogram per cubic metre, usually abbreviated as kg m^{-3}.

To use an equation:

__STEP 1__ Write down the equation and the values of the known quantities.

__STEP 2__ Rearrange the equation so the unknown quantity is the subject of the equation.

Answers

1. a)(i) 0.500 m   (ii) 320 cm   (iii) 9.560 m   b)(i) 450 g
   (ii) 1.997 kg   (iii) 5.4×10^7 g
2. a) 1.50×10^9 m   b) 3.15×10^7 s   c) 6.30×10^{-7} m
   d) 2.57×10^{-8} kg   e) 1.50×10^6 m   f) 1.245×10^{-6} m
3. a) 20 m s^{-1} b) 20 m s^{-1} c) 1.5×10^8 m s^{-1}
4. a) 3.01×10^2 b) 2.05×10^4 c) 7.85×10^{-2}

STEP 3 Substitute the known values into the rearranged equation.

STEP 4 Calculate the unknown quantity and write down its numerical value and unit.

Rearranging equations is a skill best learned by repeated practice. The most important point to remember when rearranging an equation is to do the same to both sides of the equation at each stage. Here are two examples which are different even though they look almost the same to start with.

1. Rearrange $a(y + b) = c$ to give an expression for y in terms of a, b, and c.

   Divide both sides by a to give $(y + b) = \dfrac{c}{a}$

   Subtract b from both sides to give $y = \dfrac{c}{a} - b$

2. Rearrange $ay + b = c$ to give an expression for y in terms of a, b and c.

   Subtract b from both sides to give $ay = c - b$

   Divide both sides by a to give $y = \dfrac{c - b}{a}$

WORKED EXAMPLE

Calculate the mass of a steel block of volume $0.25\ \text{m}^3$ and density $7900\ \text{kg m}^{-3}$.

Solution

$\rho = \dfrac{m}{V}$. $V = 0.25\ \text{m}^3$, $\rho = 7900\ \text{kg m}^{-3}$

Rearranging gives $m = \rho V = 7900 \times 0.25 = 1975\ \text{kg}$

WORKED EXAMPLE

The area A of a circle of diameter d is given by the formula $A = \dfrac{\pi d^2}{4}$. Calculate the diameter of a circular plate of area $0.10\ \text{m}^2$.

Solution

Rearrange the equation to give $d^2 = \dfrac{4A}{\pi}$.

Substituting $A = 0.10\ \text{m}^2$ gives

$d^2 = \dfrac{4 \times 0.10}{\pi} = 0.127\ \text{m}^2$

Hence $d = \sqrt{0.127} = 0.36\ \text{m}$

Questions (see below for answers)

1. Rearrange each of the equations below to make z the subject of each equation.

   a) $az + b = c$ b) $\dfrac{(z + p)}{q} = r$ c) $\dfrac{z}{k} - m = n$

2. a) Rearrange $V = IR$ to make (i) I the subject, (ii) R the subject of the equation.
   b) Rearrange $v = u + at$ to make (i) a a subject, (ii) t the subject.
   c) Rearrange $s = \dfrac{at^2}{2}$ to make (i) a the subject, (ii) t the subject.
3. Rearrange each formula below to make r the subject.
   a) The area of a circle of radius r, $A = \pi r^2$
   b) The surface area of a sphere of radius r, $A = 4\pi r^2$
   c) The volume of a cylinder of radius r and height H, $V = \pi r^2 H$
   d) The volume of a sphere of radius r, $V = \dfrac{4}{3}\pi r^3$

Making measurements in physics

Here are some hints and tips on how to use the more common instruments you will use for making measurements in your physics course.

The top pan balance is used to measure mass. It needs to be level and in a draught-free environment. Its read-out can easily be checked using a set of standard masses. Most top-pan balances have more than one range. To avoid overloading a balance, always use the highest range first and then select the most appropriate range for the object under test. A 'tare' button on the balance enables the read-out to be set to zero with a beaker on the pan. If the beaker is then removed, filled and replaced, the read-out gives the mass of its contents directly. The precision of a balance (e.g. to 0.01 g) is given by the least significant figure on the read-out.

Fig 2.1 The top pan balance

Answers

1. a) $\dfrac{(c - b)}{a}$ b) $qr - p$ c) $k(n + m)$

2. (a)(i) $I = \dfrac{V}{R}$ (ii) $R = \dfrac{V}{I}$ b)(i) $a = \dfrac{(v - u)}{t}$ (ii) $t = \dfrac{(v - u)}{a}$

   (c)(i) $a = \dfrac{2s}{t^2}$ (ii) $t = \left(\dfrac{2s}{a}\right)^{1/2}$

3. a) $r = \left(\dfrac{A}{\pi}\right)^{1/2}$ b) $r = \left(\dfrac{4A}{\pi}\right)^{1/2}$ c) $r = \left(\dfrac{V}{\pi H}\right)^{1/2}$ d) $r = \left(\dfrac{3V}{4\pi}\right)^{1/2}$

6

A vernier is used to measure the length of an object to within 0.1 mm, for lengths up to about 200 mm. It may be used to measure the external diameter or the internal diameter of a pipe. Figure 6.6 (p. 48) shows how to read a vernier scale.

Each interval of the slider scale is 0.9 mm. This is so that the position of the zero of the slider scale beyond the nearest millimetre mark on the main scale can be determined by seeing where a mark on the slider scale is aligned with a millimetre mark on the main scale.

A micrometer is used to measure lengths to within 0.01 mm, up to about 50 mm. Figure 6.5 (p. 48) shows how to use and read a micrometer. Each complete turn of the barrel alters the gap by 0.5 mm exactly. There are usually 50 equal divisions on the barrel scale so that each division corresponds to 0.01 mm. If used to measure the diameter of a wire, several readings at different positions should be made and an average value calculated.

Density experiments

Regular solids

Measure the mass and dimensions of rectangular and cylindrical blocks of different materials. Calculate the volume of each object using the appropriate formula from Fig 2.2 below. Use your results to calculate the density of each object, using the formula

$$\text{density} = \frac{\text{mass}}{\text{volume}}$$

If possible, use a data book of density values to identify the material of each object. Record your measurements and calculations.

Liquids

Measure the mass of a given quantity of liquid using a suitable beaker and a top pan balance. Also, measure the volume of the liquid using a suitable measuring cylinder, as in Fig 2.3. Hence calculate the density of the liquid.

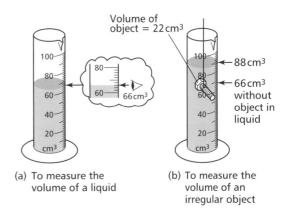

(a) To measure the volume of a liquid

(b) To measure the volume of an irregular object

Fig 2.3 Using a measuring cylinder

Irregular objects

Measure the mass of the object. Then suspend the object on a thread and immerse it in water in a measuring cylinder. The rise of the water level is equal to the volume of the object. Hence calculate the density of the object.

> **Reminder**
> Note on units: Give your density values in $kg\ m^{-3}$. Use the conversion factors on p. 4 to convert from grams to kilograms etc. Measuring cylinders are calibrated in cm^3. To calculate a volume in m^3, divide the volume in cm^3 by 10^6. Note that $1\ g\ cm^{-3} = 1000\ kg\ m^{-3}$.

 Questions (see below for answers)

1. A rectangular steel block has dimensions 120 mm × 40 mm × 25 mm. Its mass is 950 g. Calculate a) its mass in kilograms, b) its volume in m^3, c) its density in $kg\ m^{-3}$.
2. A solid metal cylinder of diameter 32 mm and length 11 mm has a mass of 24 g. Calculate a) its mass in kilograms, b) its volume in m^3, c) its density in $kg\ m^{-3}$.
3. An empty tin of mass 140 g of internal diameter 100 mm was filled to a depth of 90 mm with paint. The total mass of the tin and contents was 2.400 kg.
   Calculate a) the mass of paint in the tin, b) the volume of paint in the tin, c) the density of the paint.

 Using trigonometry

You will meet the three trigonometry functions frequently in your physics course. You need to remember how each function is defined from the right-angle triangle equations as shown in Fig 2.4 and make sure you know how to use these equations.

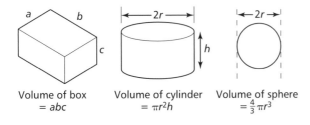

| | | |
Volume of box = abc Volume of cylinder = $\pi r^2 h$ Volume of sphere = $\frac{4}{3}\pi r^3$

Figure 2.2 Volume formulae

Answers

1. a) 0.95 kg b) $1.20 \times 10^{-4}\ m^3$ c) 7920 kg m^{-3}
2. a) 0.024 kg b) $8.9 \times 10^{-6}\ m^3$ c) 2710 kg m^{-3}
3. a) 2.260 kg b) $7.1 \times 10^{-4}\ m^3$ c) 3200 kg m^{-3}

In addition, you need to make sure you can use the trigonometry buttons on your calculator, including

- the 'inv' button to find the inverse of each function (e.g. the angle whose sin is 0.5 = inv sin 0.5 = 30°)
- the 'mode' button to make sure the calculator works angles out in degrees.

Angles can be expressed either in degrees or in radians. The radian scale is defined on the basis of 2π radians = 360 degrees. The top of a calculator display indicates 'deg' when the calculator is operating in its degree mode. If it indicates 'rad', press the 'mode' button to switch from radian mode into degree mode.

You will also meet Pythagoras' equation for the right-angle triangle frequently in your physics course. In terms of the right-angle triangle in Fig 2.4, the equation is $o^2 + a^2 = h^2$.

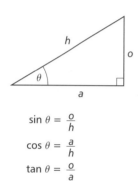

$$\sin \theta = \frac{o}{h}$$

$$\cos \theta = \frac{a}{h}$$

$$\tan \theta = \frac{o}{a}$$

Fig 2.4 The three trigonometry functions

Plotting and using straight line graphs

The equation for a straight line is $y = mx + c$, where m is the gradient and c is the intercept on the y-axis. If the line passes through the origin, then $c = 0$ and the above equation becomes $y = mx$. In this case where the line passes through the origin, the two variables are proportional to each other.

Two related physical variables are said to have a **linear** relationship if measured values give a straight line when plotted on a graph. For example, Fig 2.6 shows how the length of a spring changes when it supports different weights. The extension of the spring (= change of length) is proportional to the weight it supports. This relationship is known as **Hooke's law**.

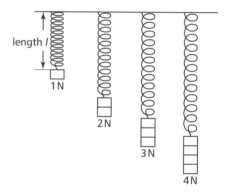

Fig 2.6 Extending a spring

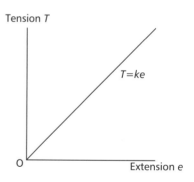

Fig 2.7 Hooke's Law

Figure 2.6 can be converted into a graph of tension T in the spring against extension e of the spring (Fig 2.7) since the tension in the spring is equal and opposite to the weight when the spring is at rest. The line in Fig 2.7 passes through the origin

Questions (see below for answers)

1. a) Calculate $\sin \theta$, $\cos \theta$ and $\tan \theta$ for θ equal to (i) 30°, (ii) 60°.
   b) Calculate θ in degrees for (i) $\sin \theta = 0.5$, (ii) $\cos \theta = 0.5$, (iii) $\tan \theta = 0.5$.
2. Calculate the unknown sides in Fig 2.5 for a) $\theta = 30°$ and $a = 4.0$ cm, b) $\theta = 45°$ and $b = 30$ mm, c) $\theta = 60°$ and $c = 25$ mm.

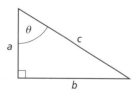

Fig 2.5

Answers

1. a) (sin, cos, tan) (i) 0.5, 0.866, 0.577, (ii) 0.866, 0.5, 1.732, b)(i) 30°, 60°, 26.6°

2. a) $b = 2.3$ cm, $c = 4.62$ cm, b) $a = 30$ mm, $c = 42.4$ mm, c) $a = 12.5$ mm, $b = 21.7$ mm

so this line can be described by the equation $T = ke$, where the 'spring constant' k is the gradient of the line. This is the equation for Hooke's law.

Experiment: To measure the spring constant of a steel spring

Arrange the spring as shown in Fig 2.8. Measure the length of the spring when it is at rest with different known weights suspended from it. Plot your measurements on a graph of tension (= weight) on the vertical axis and extension (= change of length) on the horizontal axis. Determine the spring constant as described in Fig 2.7.

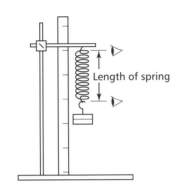

Fig 2.8 Testing a spring

 Question (see below for answer)

The following measurements were made of the length of a vertical steel spring when different known weights were suspended from it.

Tension (=weight)/N	0	2	4	6	8
Spring length/mm	300	350	402	448	500
Extension/mm	0		102		

a) Complete the Table by calculating the extension for the missing entries.
b) (i) Plot a graph of tension on the vertical axis against extension on the horizontal axis.
   (ii) Use your graph to determine the spring constant k of the spring in N m^{-1}.

Summary

✔ **The SI system** of scientific units is based on the metre, the kilogram, the second, the ampere (electric current) and the kelvin (temperature). All other units are derived from these five base units.

✔ **Prefixes** commonly used in science are nano- (n), micro- (µ), milli- (m), kilo- (k), mega- (M) and giga- (G) representing 10^{-9}, 10^{-6}, 10^{-3}, 10^{3}, 10^{6} and 10^{9} respectively.

✔ **Commonly-used instruments** in physics include the vernier and the micrometer (lengths), the top pan balance (mass), the stopwatch (time intervals) and the measuring cylinder (volume).

✔ **Area and volume formulae**
   ● The area of a circle of radius $r = \pi r^2$.
   ● The surface area of a sphere of radius $r = 4\pi r^2$.
   ● The volume of a rectangular block = length × width × height.
   ● The volume of a cylinder of radius r and height $H = \pi r^2 H$.
   ● The volume of a sphere of radius $r = \frac{4}{3}\pi r^3$.

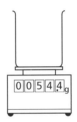 **TEST QUESTIONS** (see p. 69 for answers)

1. Which of the following instruments, **A** to **E**, would you use to measure
   a) the thickness of a coin?   b) the mass of a beaker?   c) the volume of a liquid?   d) the diameter of a wire?
   A vernier; **B** top pan balance; **C** measuring cylinder; **D** mm rule; **E** micrometer

2. a) The figure below shows a top pan balance with an empty beaker on it. The balance read zero before the beaker was placed on the pan. What is the mass of the beaker?

b) The beaker was removed and partly filled with liquid. When the beaker was replaced on the pan, the read-out displayed 177 g. Calculate the mass of liquid in the beaker.
c) The liquid was poured into a measuring cylinder as shown below.

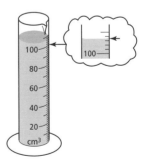

What is the volume of the liquid in the measuring cylinder?
d) Calculate the density of the liquid.

Answer

b)(ii) $k = 40$ N m^{-1}

3. A rectangular metal plate of thickness 2.5 mm is 50 mm long and 65 mm wide. Its mass is 60 g. Calculate
   a) the distance round its edge, in metres,
   b) the area of one of its flat faces, in m^2,
   c) its volume, in m^3,
   d) its density, in kg m^{-3}.

4. A solid aluminium rod of length 0.2 m has a uniform diameter of 52 mm. The density of aluminium is 2700 kg m^{-3}. Calculate
   a) its volume, in m^3,
   b) its mass, in kg.

5. a) Calculate the volume of a steel sphere of diameter 12 mm.
   b) Calculate the diameter of a steel sphere of volume 4.80 cm^3.

3 | Model answers to selected questions

Questions are selected from *New Understanding Physics for Advanced Level, Fourth Edition* (even-numbered questions only).

Chapter 1

2. a) Rearrange $v = \dfrac{s}{t}$ to give

$$s = vt = 3.00 \times 10^8 \text{ m s}^{-1}$$
$$\times (365.25 \times 24 \times 60 \times 60 \text{ s})$$
$$= 9.47 \times 10^{15} \text{ m} \checkmark$$

b) Rearrange $v = \dfrac{s}{t}$ to give

$$t = \frac{s}{v} = \frac{150 \times 10^6 \times 1000 \text{ m}}{3.00 \times 10^8 \text{ m s}^{-1}} = 500 \text{ s} \checkmark$$

c) The distance round the orbit $s = 2\pi r$ where the radius of the orbit, $r = 150 \times 10^6$ km $\checkmark$

$$\therefore \quad v = \frac{s}{t} = \frac{2\pi \times 150 \times 10^6 \times 1000}{365.25 \times 24 \times 60 \times 60}$$
$$= 2.99 \times 10^4 \text{ m s}^{-1} \checkmark$$

4. Distance travelled in

12 hours = speed × time
$$= 8.0 \text{ km h}^{-1} \times 12 \text{ h} = 96.0 \text{ km} \checkmark$$

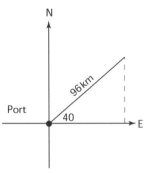

Using the diagram above, the distance moved due
North = 96 sin 40 = 61.7 km $\checkmark$
the distance moved due
East = 96 cos 40 = 73.5 km $\checkmark$

6. Method 1: After 1 hour, A is 15 km due North of the port and B is 10 km from the port in a direction N60°E. Using the diagram below, B is therefore a distance of 10 cos 60 due N of the port and a distance 10 sin 60 due east of the port.

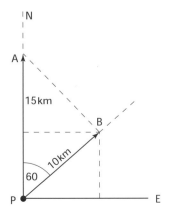

∴ B is 5 km (= 15 − 10 cos 60) further South and 8.7 km (= 10 sin 60) further East than A.
a) The distance from A to B is therefore
$\sqrt{(5^2 + 8.7^2)} = 10.0$ km after 1 hour.

Let the angle between the line AB and the

North-South line = θ; $\quad \therefore \quad \tan \theta = \dfrac{8.7}{5}$

$\therefore \theta = 60°$

b) The velocity of B relative to A
$$= \frac{\text{distance AB}}{\text{time}} = \frac{10.0 \text{ km}}{1 \text{ hour}} = 10 \text{ km h}^{-1}$$

Method 2: Velocity of A, $V_A = (15, 0)$ km h^{-1}
Velocity of B, $V_B = (10 \cos 60, 10 \sin 60)$ km h^{-1}
∴ relative velocity of B with respect to A
$$= V_B - V_A = (10 \cos 60 - 15, -10 \sin 60) \text{ km h}^{-1}$$
$$= (-5.0, -8.7) \text{ km h}^{-1}$$
∴ the speed of B relative to A
$$= \sqrt{(5^2 + 8.7^2)} = 10 \text{ km h}^{-1}$$
∴ the distance from A to B after 1 hour = 10 km.
See Method 1 to work out the direction of B from A.

8. The flight time = distance/speed
$$= \frac{4800 \times 1000 \text{ m}}{400 \text{ m s}^{-1}} = 12000 \text{ s} = 3 \text{ h } 20 \text{ min}$$
∴ The London-bound Concorde arrived at London at 13.00 GMT. The NY bound Concorde arrived at 13.00 NY time which is 18.00 GMT. This Concorde therefore left London at 14.40 GMT.

10. Velocity of boat relative to water
V_{bw} = velocity of boat − velocity of water
$$= (v_1, 0) - (0, 0.9) = (v_1, -0.9)$$
where v_1, is the component of the boat's velocity perpendicular to the flow and its parallel component is zero. See diagram below.

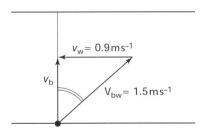

Since the boat's speed relative to the water = 1.5 m s^{-1}, then the magnitude of $V_{bw} = 1.5$ m s^{-1}
$\therefore v_1^2 + (-0.9)^2 = 1.5^2$ so $v_1^2 = 2.25 - 0.81 = 1.44$
hence $v_1 = 1.2$ m s^{-1}
Time taken to cross 500 m directly
= 500 m/1.2 m s^{-1} = 417 s.
Angle of boat's velocity to direct path
= inv tan 0.9/1.2 = 37°

12. a) $s_1 = 90$ km h^{-1} × (20/60) h = 30 km, ✓
$s_2 = 15$ km, $s_3 = 30$ km
∴ Total distance = 75 km ✓
b) $t_1 = 20$ min, $t_2 = 25$ min,

$$t_3 = \frac{\text{distance}}{\text{speed}} = \frac{30 \text{ km}}{80 \text{ km h}^{-1}}$$

= 0.375 h = 22.5 min ✓
∴ Total time = 67.5 min ✓

c) Average speed = $\dfrac{\text{total distance}}{\text{total time}}$

$$= \frac{75 \text{ km}}{(67.5/60) \text{ h}} = 67 \text{ km h}^{-1} ✓$$

14. $u = 110$ m s^{-1}, $v = 0$, $s = 0.065$ m
a) To find t, use $s = \frac{1}{2}(u + v)t$ with $v = 0$ to give
$s = \frac{1}{2}ut$ ✓
Rearranging this equation gives

$$t = \frac{2s}{u} = \frac{2 \times 0.065 \text{ m}}{110 \text{ m s}^{-1}} = 1.2 \times 10^{-3} \text{ s} ✓$$

b) To find a, use $v = u + at$ with $v = 0$ to give
$0 = u + at$
Rearranging this equation gives $at = -u$

$$∴ \quad a = -\frac{u}{t} ✓$$

$$= -\frac{110 \text{ m s}^{-1}}{1.2 \times 10^{-3} \text{ s}} = -9.3 \times 10^4 \text{ m s}^{-2} ✓$$

16. $u = 0$, $s = 500$ m, $v = 22$ m s^{-1}
a) To find t, use $s = \frac{1}{2}(u + v)t$ with $u = 0$ to give
$s = \frac{1}{2}vt$ ✓
Rearranging this equation gives

$$t = \frac{2s}{v} = \frac{2 \times 500 \text{ m}}{22 \text{ m s}^{-1}} = 45.5 \text{ s} ✓$$

b) See the diagram below. ✓ for correct shape,
✓ for correct labels on axes, ✓ for correct
scales.

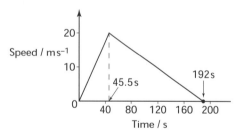

c) Stage 1:

$$a = \frac{v - u}{t} = \frac{(22 - 0) \text{ m s}^{-1}}{45.5 \text{ s}} = 0.48 \text{ m s}^{-2} ✓$$

Stage 2:

$$a = \frac{v - u}{t} = \frac{0 - 22 \text{ m s}^{-1}}{(192 - 45.5) \text{ s}} = 0.15 \text{ m s}^{-2} ✓$$

Average speed in each stage = 11 m s^{-1} ✓
∴ Overall average speed = 11 m s^{-1} ✓
(Note: An alternative method for calculating the
average speed is to work out the distance in each
stage to give the total distance moved. The total
distance divided by the total time gives the
average speed:
Distance moved in stage 1 = 11 × 45.5 = 500 m
Distance moved in stage 2
= 11(192 − 45.5) = 1612 m
Total distance moved = 2112 m
∴ Overall average speed = 2112 m/192 s = 11 m s^{-1})

18. $u = 0$, $t = 1.8$ s, $a = -9.8$ m s^{-2} (− for downwards)
a) To find s, use $s = ut + \frac{1}{2}at^2$ with $u = 0$ to give
$s = \frac{1}{2}at^2$ ✓
∴ $s = -\frac{1}{2} \times 9.8 \times 1.8^2 = -15.9$ m (i.e. 15.9 m
downwards) ✓
b) To find v, use $v = u + at$ with $u = 0$ to give
$v = at$ ✓
∴ $v = 0 - 9.8 \times 1.8 = -17.6$ m s^{-1} ✓

20. a) $u = 0$, $a = -9.8$ m s^{-2}, $s = -14.5$ m
To find v, use $v^2 = u^2 + 2as$ with $u = 0$ to give
$v^2 = 2as$ ✓
∴ $v^2 = -2 \times 9.8 \times -14.5 = 284$
∴ $v = 16.9$ m s^{-1} ✓
b) In the sand, $u = -16.9$ m s^{-1}, $v = 0$,
$s = -0.185$ m
To find a, use $v^2 = u^2 + 2as$ with $v = 0$ to give
$u^2 = -2as$ ✓

$$∴ a = \frac{-u^2}{2s} = -\frac{16.9^2}{2 \times -0.185} = 768 \text{ m s}^{-2} \text{ upwards.}$$

22. For the sketch graph, see diagram below.

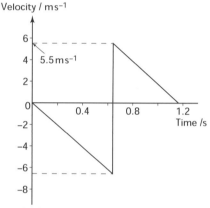

✓✓✓ for 3 lines as above
✓ for correct scales
✓ for correct negative gradient

a) (i) For the descent $u = 0$, $a = -9.8$ m s^{-2},
$s = -2.0$ m
To find t, use $s = ut + \frac{1}{2}at^2$ with $u = 0$ to give
$s = \frac{1}{2}at^2$ ✓

$$∴ t^2 = \frac{2s}{a} = \frac{2 \times -2.0}{-9.8} = 0.408 ✓$$

∴ $t = 0.64$ s ✓

(ii) For the rise, $v = 0$, $a = -9.8$ m s^{-2}, $s = +1.5$ m
To find t, $v = u + at$ with $v = 0$ ∴ $u + at = 0$
gives $u = -at$
Use $s = ut + \frac{1}{2}at^2$ with $u = -at$ to give
$s = -\frac{1}{2}at^2$ ✓

$$∴ t^2 = \frac{-2s}{a} = \frac{-2 \times 1.5}{-9.8} = 0.306 ✓$$

∴ $t = 0.55$ s ✓

Add answers to (i) and (ii) to give 1.19 s for the
total time. ✓
Note: alternative for (ii) is to use $v^2 = u^2 + 2as$
to find u, then use $v = u + at$ to find a.
b) Just after impact, the ball's initial speed = u;
$a = -9.8$ m s^{-2}, $v = 0$ at top, $s = 1.5$ m
Use $v^2 = u^2 + 2as$ with $v = 0$ to give $u^2 = -2as$
∴ $u^2 = -2 \times -9.8 \times 1.5 = 29.4$ ✓
∴ $u = 5.4$ m s^{-1}

Note
Question 24   If you have successfully worked
through questions 17, 19, 21 and 23, you ought to
be able to do question 24.
Questions 26 and 28   See the textbook on p. 14
for a worked example on projectile motion in
2 dimensions.

Chapter 2

2. a) $F = \dfrac{mv - mu}{t} = \dfrac{0.25 \times 20 - 0}{0.1} = 50 \text{ N}$ ✓

   $s = \frac{1}{2}(u + v)t = \frac{1}{2} \times 20 \times 0.1 = 1.0 \text{ m}$ ✓

   b) Rearrange $s = \frac{1}{2}(u + v)t$ to give

   $t = \dfrac{2s}{(u + v)}$ ✓ $= \dfrac{2 \times 0.1}{20} = 0.01 \text{ s}$ ✓

   $\therefore F = \dfrac{mv - mu}{t} = \dfrac{0.25 \times 0 - 0.25 \times 20}{0.01}$ ✓

   $= -500 \text{ N}$

4. a) $u = 0$, $v = 9.5 \text{ m s}^{-1}$, $s = 8.0 \text{ m}$

   To find t, rearrange $s = \frac{1}{2}(u + v)t$ to give

   $t = \dfrac{2s}{(u + v)}$ ✓ $= \dfrac{2 \times 8.0 \, m}{(0 + 9.5)} = 1.68 \, s$ ✓

   b) To find a, rearrange $v = u + at$ to give

   $a = \dfrac{(v - u)}{t}$ ✓ $= 5.64 \, m \, s^{-2}$ ✓

   c) To find F, use $F = ma = 65 \times 5.64 = 367 \text{ N}$ ✓

6. Use $T - mg = ma$ where $+$ is up and $-$ is down. See diagram below.

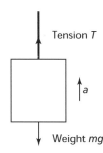

Tension T

a

Weight mg

   a) Total mass $= 480 \text{ kg} + (3000/g) = 786 \text{ kg}$ ✓
   $T = mg + ma = (786 \times 9.8) + (480 \times 0)$ ✓
   $= 7704 \text{ N}$ ✓

   b) $a = -1.5 \text{ m s}^{-2}$ (– for downwards)
   $\therefore T = mg + ma = (786 \times 9.8) + (786 \times -1.5)$ ✓
   $= 6525 \text{ N}$ ✓

   c) $a = +1.5 \text{ m s}^{-2}$ as motion is downwards and the lift is decelerating so acceleration is upwards.
   $\therefore T = mg + ma = (786 \times 9.8) + (786 \times 1.5)$ ✓
   $= 8882 \text{ N}$ ✓

   d) $a = +1.5 \text{ m s}^{-2}$ as motion is upwards and lift is accelerating.
   $\therefore T = mg + ma = (786 \times 9.8) + (786 \times 1.5)$ ✓
   $= 8882 \text{ N}$ ✓

   e) $a = -1.5 \text{ m s}^{-2}$ as motion is upward and the lift is decelerating.
   $\therefore T = mg + ma = (786 \times 9.8) + (786 \times -1.5)$ ✓
   $= 6525 \text{ N}$ ✓

8. See diagram below.

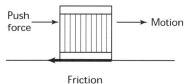

Push force   Motion

Friction

   a) The friction force reduced its speed from 1.5 m s^{-1} to rest in 1.2 m.
   $u = 1.5 \text{ m s}^{-1}$, $v = 0$, $s = 1.2 \text{ m}$, $m = 40 \text{ kg}$
   Firstly, find a by rearranging $v^2 = u^2 + 2as$ to give

   $a = \dfrac{v^2 - u^2}{2s} = \dfrac{0 - 1.5^2}{2 \times 1.2}$ ✓ $= 0.94 \text{ m s}^{-2}$ ✓

   To find F, use $F = ma = 40 \times 0.94 = 37.5 \text{ N}$ ✓

   b) Distance moved in 1 s at steady speed $= 1.5$ m.
   $W = Fs = 37.5 \times 1.5 = 56.3 \text{ J}$ ✓

10. a) **Either** draw a scale diagram as shown below to give an answer of 13.9 kN ✓ along the mid-line. ✓

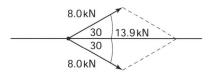

8.0 kN

30   13.9 kN

30

8.0 kN

   Or since both forces act at 30° to the mid-line ✓, each force in kN has a component parallel to the mid-line of 8 cos 30 and a component perpendicular to the mid-line of 8 sin 30. The perpendicular components are in opposite directions so they cancel each other out. The resultant in kN is therefore $2 \times 8 \cos 30$ along the midline.
   $\therefore$ combined force $= 16 \cos 30 = 13.9 \text{ kN}$ ✓

   b) Since the ship is moving at steady speed, the drag force is equal and opposite to the combined effect of the two cable forces. ✓
   $\therefore$ the drag force $= 13.9 \text{ kN}$ ✓

   c) When the ship is moving at steady speed being pulled by both cables, the pull of each cable and the drag force cancel out. ✓
   The pull in one cable + the drag force is therefore equal and opposite to the pull of 8 kN in the other cable. ✓
   If this cable snaps, the combined effect of the other two forces (i.e. 8 kN) acts unopposed. ✓

12. $u = 80 \text{ m s}^{-1}$, $v = 0$, $s = 0.025 \text{ m}$, $m = 0.001 \text{ kg}$

   a) To find t, rearrange $s = \frac{1}{2}(u + v)t$ to give

   $t = \dfrac{2s}{(u + v)}$ ✓ $= \dfrac{2 \times 0.025}{(80 + 0)} = 6.25 \times 10^{-4} \text{ s}$ ✓

   b) Initial momentum $= mu = 0.001 \times 80$
   $= 0.08 \text{ kg m s}^{-1}$ ✓
   Final momentum $= mv = 0.001 \times 0 = 0$ ✓
   $\therefore$ Change of momentum
   $= mv - mu = -0.08 \text{ kg m s}^{-1}$ ✓

   c) Force $F = \dfrac{mv - mu}{t} = -\dfrac{0.08 \text{ kg m s}^{-1}}{6.25 \times 10^{-4} \text{ s}}$ ✓

   $= 128 \text{ N}$ ✓

14. See diagrams.

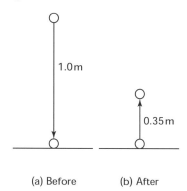

(a) Before   (b) After

a) Gain of k.e. = loss of p.e. $\therefore \frac{1}{2}mu^2 = mgh$ ✓
where u is the speed just before impact and h is the height drop.
$\therefore u = (2gh)^{1/2} = (2 \times 9.8 \times 1.0)^{1/2} = 4.43$ m s^{-1} ✓
downwards = -4.43 m s^{-1}

b) Loss of k.e. = gain of p.e. $\therefore \frac{1}{2}mv^2 = mgh$ ✓
where v is the speed just after impact and h is the height drop.
$\therefore v = (2gh)^{1/2} = (2 \times 9.8 \times 0.35)^{1/2}$
$= 2.61$ m s^{-1} ✓ upwards = $+2.61$ m s^{-1}

c) Change of momentum = $mv - mu$
$= (0.15 \times 2.61) - (0.15 \times -4.43)$
$= 1.06$ kg m s^{-1} ✓

d) Force = $\dfrac{\text{chance of momentum}}{\text{impact time}} = \dfrac{1.06 \text{ kg m s}^{-1}}{0.080 \text{ s}}$
$= 13.2$ kg m s^{-2} ✓

16. a) Since the water reaches a height of 20 m when it is directed vertically upwards, its initial speed u on leaving the jet can be calculated since final speed $v = 0$
acceleration $a = -9.8$ m s^{-2}
displacement $s = 20$ m. ✓
$\therefore$ using $v^2 = u^2 + 2as$ with $v = 0$ gives
$u^2 = -2as$ ✓
$\therefore u^2 = -2 \times -9.8 \times 20 = 392$
$\therefore u = 19.8$ m s^{-1} ✓

b) In 1 second, the volume of water leaving the jet = uA where A = area of cross-section of the jet. ✓
$\therefore$ mass of water leaving per second
= volume/second × density of water = $uA\rho$,
where p is the density of the water. ✓
$\therefore$ mass of water leaving per second
$= 19.8 \times 4 \times 10^{-4} \times 1000 = 7.9$ kg s^{-1} ✓

c) Momentum leaving in 1 second
= mass leaving in 1 second
× exit velocity (u) ✓
$= 7.9 \times 19.8 = 157$ kg m s^{-1} ✓

d) Force = momentum loss per second = 157 N ✓

18. Let due N be the +y direction and due E the +x direction, as in the diagram below.

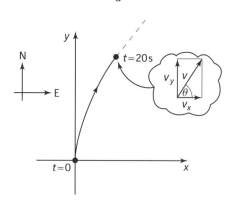

a) y-direction: $v_y = 4$ m s^{-1} throughout since there is no force component in the y-direction.
x-direction: acceleration in the x-direction,
$$a_x = \frac{\text{force component in the } x\text{-direction}}{\text{mass}}$$
$\therefore a_x = \dfrac{0.10 \text{ N}}{2.5 \text{ kg}} = 0.04$ m s^{-2} ✓
$u_x = 0, t = 20$ s $\quad \therefore v_x = u_x + a_x t = 0 + 0.04 \times 20$
$= 0.80$ m s^{-1} ✓
Speed $v = (v_x^2 + v_y^2)^{1/2} = (0.80^2 + 4.0^2)^{1/2}$
$= 4.1$ m s^{-1} ✓
Direction of motion is at an angle θ to the x-axis where $\tan\theta = v_y/v_x = 0.80/4.0 = 0.20$
$\therefore \theta = $ inv tan $0.20 = 11.3°$ ✓

b) Gain of kinetic energy
$= \frac{1}{2}mv^2 - \frac{1}{2}mu^2$
$= \frac{1}{2} \times 2.5 \times (4.0^2 + 0.8^2) - \frac{1}{2} \times 2.5 \times 4.0^2$ ✓
$= \frac{1}{2} \times 2.5 \times 0.8^2 = 0.80$ J ✓

c) Distance moved in x-direction,
$s_x = u_x t + \frac{1}{2}a_x t^2 = 0 + \frac{1}{2} \times 0.04 \times 20^2$ ✓
$= 8.0$ m ✓
Note: $F_x s_x$ = work done by the force = gain of k.e.
$\therefore s_x = $ gain of k.e./force $= 0.80/0.10 = 8.0$ m

20. Look at the diagram below.

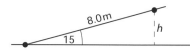

a) Distance moved in 1 s along incline = 8.0 m
$\therefore$ height gain for 8.0 m along the incline
$= 8.0 \sin 15 = 2.07$ m
$\therefore$ gain of p.e. in 1 second
$= mgh = 7000$ N × 2.07 m = 14.5 kJ

b) Work done in 1 second against friction
= frictional force × distance moved in 1 s
= 500 N × 8.0 m = 4.0 kJ

c) K.e. gain per second = 0 since the car is moving at constant speed.
$\therefore$ Work done in 1 second by engine
= gain of p.e. per second + work done against friction per second
= 14.5 + 4.0 = 18.4 kJ
$\therefore$ Engine power = 18.4 kW

22. a) Horizontal component of initial velocity = vertical component of initial velocity since it is projected at 45°. Let U_h = horizontal component of initial velocity

∴ horizontal distance moved = $U_h t$ where t is the time taken

∴ $U_h t = 60$ ✓

Vertical component of its initial velocity = $U_v = U_h$

∴ Time to reach maximum height, $t/2 = U_h/g$

∴ $t = 2U_h/g$

∴ $U_h(2U_h/g) = 60$

$2U_h{}^2/g = 60$ ∴ $U_h{}^2 = 30\,g = 294$ m^2 s^{-2} ✓

Initial k.e. $= \frac{1}{2}mU_h{}^2 + \frac{1}{2}mU_v{}^2 = 2 \times (\frac{1}{2} \times 1.5 \times 294)$

$= 441$ J ✓ (or 450 J if $g = 10$ m s^{-2} is used)

b) Power = gain of k.e./ time taken

$= \frac{1}{2} \times 60 \times 10^2/2.5$ ✓ $= 1200$ W ✓

Note
Questions 24 and 26 See the worked example in the textbook on p. 27.
Question 28 See the notes in the textbook on p. 22.

Chapter 3

2. 6 N ✓ because the removed force (6 N) was equal (and opposite) to the other two forces. ✓

4. a) Let θ = the angle between the vertical and either of the 0.40 m strings as shown in the diagram below.

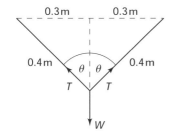

$\sin\theta = \dfrac{0.3}{0.4}$ ✓

∴ $\theta = \text{inv}\sin 0.75 = 48.6°$ ✓

b) Let T = tension in each string.
Consider the forces acting on the point where the three strings are joined.
The vertical component of each tension
$= T\cos\theta$ upwards. ✓
The two vertical components of tension
$=$ weight ✓
∴ $2T\cos\theta = 6$ so $1.32\,T = 6$ ✓
∴ $T = 6/1.32 = 4.5$ N ✓

6. Anticlockwise moment about pivot
$= 1.20$ N $\times 0.45$ m $= 0.54$ N m ✓
Clockwise moment about pivot
$= W \times 0.22$ m $= 0.22\,W$ ✓
In equilibrium, clockwise moment
= anticlockwise moment
$0.22\,W = 0.54$ ✓
∴ $W = 2.45$ N ✓

8. The arrangement is shown in the diagram below.

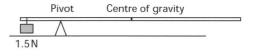

Clockwise moment about the pivot
$= W \times (0.50 - 0.24)$ m where W is the weight of the rule. ✓
(Note: the weight of the rule acts at its centre of gravity.)
Anticlockwise moment about the pivot
$= 1.50$ N $\times (0.24 - 0.04)$ m $= 0.30$ N m ✓
In equilibrium, clockwise moment
= anticlockwise moment
$0.26\,W = 0.30$ ✓
∴ $W = 1.15$ N ✓

10. Force $\times$ perpendicular distance = torque

∴ Force $= \dfrac{\text{torque}}{\text{perpendicular distance}}$

$= \dfrac{40\,N\,m}{0.02\,m} = 200$ N ✓

12. a) Pressure $= 1.2 \times 15^2 = 270$ Pa ✓
∴ Force F = pressure $\times$ side area
$= 270 \times (8 \times 15) = 32\,400$ N ✓

b) The figure below shows a front-view of the lorry. The wind tends to turn the lorry about the wheels on the other side to the side that is hit by the wind. The centre of gravity of the lorry is directly above the midpoint between directly-opposite wheels.

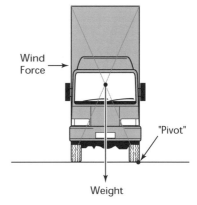

✓ for correct force diagram similar to the diagram above.
Clockwise moment about the wheels
= lorry weight $\times 0.5 \times$ wheel base
$= 1.5 \times 10^5$ N $\times 1$ m $= 1.5 \times 10^5$ N m ✓
Anticlockwise moment about the wheels
$= Fh/2 = 32\,400$ N $\times 4$ m
$= 129\,600$ N m ✓
The clockwise moment is greater than the anticlockwise moment so the lorry does not lift off the ground on one side. ✓

c) The tyre grip on the 'windward' side would be lessened which would affect the steerability of the lorry. There would be a tendency for the lorry to veer to one side. ✓

14. The figure below shows the forces acting on the block.

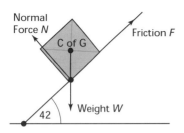

Resolving the forces parallel and perpendicular to the slope gives:
Parallel: $W \sin 42 = F$ ✓
where F is the friction force
Perpendicular: $W \cos 42 = N$ ✓
where N is the normal force
$$\mu = \frac{F}{N} = \frac{W \sin 42}{W \cos 42} = \tan 42 = 0.90 \quad ✓$$

16. a) The centre of gravity of the books is 0.15 m ($=0.5(0.4 - 0.1)$ m) from the wall. ✓
    ∴ The moment of the books about the hinge $= 50 \text{ N} \times 0.15 \text{ m} = 7.5 \text{ N m}$. ✓
    b) Take moments about the hinge.
    Clockwise moment $= 7.5 \text{ N m}$
    Anticlockwise moment $= Fd$, where F is the force of the strut on the shelf and d is the perpendicular distance from the strut to the hinge.
    Referring to the diagram, $\cos \theta = 0.4/0.5 = 0.8$
    ∴ $\theta = 47°$ ✓
    ∴ $d = 0.4 \sin \theta = 0.4 \times \sin 47 = 0.29 \text{ m}$ ✓
    Anticlockwise moment = clockwise moment about the hinge
    $Fd = 7.5$ ✓
    $$F = \frac{7.5}{0.29} = 25.9 \text{ N} \quad ✓$$

18. a) The tension T_R in the rope is equal to the weight W. ∴ $T_R = W = 200 \text{ N}$ ✓
    These two forces act at 45° to each other. Their combined effect is therefore $2 \times 200 \cos 22.5$ since the two forces are equal. ✓
    Resultant force $= 369 \text{ N}$. ✓
    b) (i) Tension, as it is being stretched. ✓
    (ii) Compression, as it is being squashed. ✓
    c) (i) Let the tension in XY $= T$ and the compressive force in XZ $= C$, as shown in the diagram below. The tension acts at 30° above the horizontal and the compressive force acts from 30° below. ✓

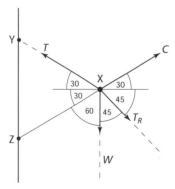

Resolving the forces at X into vertical and horizontal components:
Vertically:
$T \sin 30 + C \sin 30 = W + T_R \sin 45$ ✓
∴ $(T + C) \, 0.5 = 341$
∴ $T + C = 682$ ✓
Horizontally: $T \cos 30 = C \cos 30 + T_R \cos 45$ ✓
∴ $0.87 \, T = 0.87 \, C + 141$
∴ $T = C + 163$ ✓
Combining the two equations for T and C,
$(C + 163) + C = 682$
$2C = 682 - 163 = 519$
∴ $C = 259 \text{ N}$ ✓
∴ $T = 422 \text{ N}$ ✓

20. See the diagram below for the force diagram on the ladder. ✓

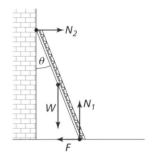

Consider the vertical and horizontal components of the forces on the ladder separately.
Vertically: $W = N_1$ ∴ $N_1 = 500 \text{ N}$ ✓
Horizontally: $F = N_2$ ✓
Since $F = \mu N_1$ at the point of slipping, then
$F = 0.2 \times 500 = 100 \text{ N}$ ✓
∴ $N_2 = 100 \text{ N}$ ✓
Taking moments about the point of contact at the floor gives:
Clockwise moment $= N_2 h$ where h is the height of the top end of the ladder above the floor. ✓
Anticlockwise moment $= Wb/2$ where b is the distance from the bottom of the wall to the foot of the ladder. ✓
In equilibrium, clockwise moment = anticlockwise moment for no slip:
$N_2 h = Wb/2$ ✓
$\tan \theta = b/h$ ✓ $= 2N_2/W = (2 \times 100)/500 = 0.4$ ✓
∴ $\theta = 21.8°$ ✓

Chapter 7

2. a) extension $= 450 - 250 \text{ mm} = 0.200 \text{ m}$ ✓
   $$\therefore k = \frac{weight}{extension} = \frac{5.0 \text{ N}}{0.200 \text{ m}} = 25.0 \text{ N m}^{-1} \quad ✓$$
   b) $\Delta e = 500 - 450 \text{ mm} = 0.050 \text{ m}$ ✓
   ∴ $\Delta W = k\Delta e = 25.0 \text{ N m}^{-1} \times 0.050 \text{ m}$
   $= 1.25 \text{ N}$ ✓
   c) $W = ke = 25.0 \text{ N m}^{-1} \times 0.050 \text{ m} = 1.25 \text{ N}$ ✓

4. $d = 0.50 \text{ mm}$ ∴ $A = \pi d^2/4 = \pi (0.41 \times 10^{-3})^2/4 \text{ m}^2$
   $= 1.32 \times 10^{-7} \text{ m}^2$ ✓
   $\Delta e = 0.0043 \text{ m}, l = 1.692 \text{ m},$
   $\Delta W = 75 - 5 = 70 \text{ N}$ ✓
   $$E = \frac{\Delta W \times l}{A \times \Delta e} = \frac{70 \times 1.692}{1.32 \times 10^{-7} \times 0.0043} \quad ✓$$
   $= 2.1 \times 10^{11} \text{ Pa}$ ✓

6. a) $d = 0.50$ mm
$$\therefore A = \pi d^2/4 = \pi(0.50 \times 10^{-3})^2/4 \text{ m}^2$$
$$= 1.96 \times 10^{-7} \text{ m}^2 \checkmark$$

$l = 1.84$ m, $W = 60$ N, $E = 2.0 \times 10^{11}$ N m^{-2}

Rearrange $E = \dfrac{Wl}{Ae}$ to give $e = \dfrac{Wl}{AE}$ $\checkmark$

$$\therefore e = \frac{60 \times 1.84}{1.96 \times 10^{-7} \times 2.0 \times 10^{11}} \checkmark$$
$$= 2.82 \times 10^{-3} \text{ m} = 2.82 \text{ mm} \checkmark$$

b) $\dfrac{e}{l} = \dfrac{2.82 \times 10^{-3}}{1.84} = 1.53 \times 10^{-3}$ $\checkmark$

$\therefore$ elastic limit is not exceeded so assume the energy stored = 0.5 We. $\checkmark$
Energy stored = 0.5 We
$$= 0.5 \times 60 \times 2.82 \times 10^{-3} = 8.46 \times 10^{-2} \text{ J} \checkmark$$

8. $e = 12 \times 4.2$ mm $= 50.4$ mm $= 5.04 \times 10^{-2}$ m $\checkmark$
$d = 0.50$ mm
$$\therefore A = \pi d^2/4 = \pi(0.50 \times 10^{-3})^2/4 \text{ m}^2$$
$$= 1.96 \times 10^{-7} \text{ m}^2 \checkmark$$
$l = 850$ mm $= 0.850$ m

Rearrange $E = \dfrac{Tl}{Ae}$ to give $T = \dfrac{AEe}{l}$ $\checkmark$

$$T = \frac{1.96 \times 10^{-7} \times 3 \times 10^9 \times 5.04 \times 10^{-2}}{0.850} \checkmark$$
$$= 34.9 \text{ N} \checkmark$$

10. a) Compression $= 0.5 \times 0.5$ mm $= 0.25$ mm
$$= 2.5 \times 10^{-4} \text{ m} \checkmark$$
$\therefore e = -2.5 \times 10^{-4}$ m, treating a compression as a negative extension.
Area of cross-section $A = 10 \times 20$ mm^2
$$= 200 \text{ mm}^2 = 2.00 \times 10^{-4} \text{ m}^2 \checkmark$$
Length $l = 10$ mm $= 0.010$ m $\checkmark$

Rearrange $E = \dfrac{Tl}{Ae}$ to give $T = \dfrac{AEe}{l}$ $\checkmark$

$$T = \frac{2.00 \times 10^{-4} \times 1.3 \times 10^{11} \times -2.5 \times 10^{-4}}{0.010} \checkmark$$
$$= -6.5 \times 10^5 \text{ N} \checkmark$$
The compressive force is therefore 6.5×10^5 N.

b) Elastic energy
$$= 0.5 \times \text{force} \times \text{compression} \checkmark$$
$$= 0.5 \times 6.5 \times 10^5 \times 2.5 \times 10^{-4} = 81 \text{ J} \checkmark$$

12. a) Each block of the graph represents 1 mJ
$(= 0.1 \text{ N} \times 10 \text{ mm})$ $\checkmark$
The area under the loading curve = 6.5 blocks $\checkmark$
$\therefore$ Work done to load rubber = 6.5 mJ
$(= 6.5 \times 1 \text{ mJ})$ $\checkmark$

b) Area under unloading curve = 5 blocks $\checkmark$
$\therefore$ Work done by rubber when unloaded = 5 mJ
$(= 5 \times 1 \text{ mJ})$
$\therefore$ Gain of internal energy = 6.5 − 5 = 1.5 mJ $\checkmark$

14. $2\theta = 52°$ $\therefore \theta = 26°$ $\checkmark$
Use $2d \sin \theta = m\lambda$ with $\lambda = 0.15$ nm and $m = 1$, $\checkmark$
$$\therefore d = \frac{\lambda}{2 \sin \theta} = \frac{0.15 \text{ nm}}{2 \times \sin 26} \checkmark = 0.17 \text{ nm} \checkmark$$

Chapter 9

2. $\theta = \dfrac{R - R_0}{R_{100} - R_0} \times 100 = \dfrac{26.95 - 25.40}{27.34 - 25.40} \times 100$ $\checkmark$

$= 80°$ on the centigrade scale of this thermometer. $\checkmark$

4. $R = \dfrac{c}{(T - 203)}$

At $T = 273$ K, $R_0 = \dfrac{c}{70}$ $\checkmark$

At $T = 373$ K, $R_{100} = \dfrac{c}{170}$ $\checkmark$

At $T = 300$ K, $R = \dfrac{c}{97}$ $\checkmark$

$\theta = \dfrac{R - R_0}{R_{100} - R_0} \times 100$

$R - R_0 = \dfrac{c}{97} - \dfrac{c}{70} = -0.00398c$

$R_{100} - R_0 = \dfrac{c}{170} - \dfrac{c}{70} = -0.00840c$

$\therefore \theta = \dfrac{-0.00398c}{-0.00840c} \times 100$ $\checkmark$ $= 47.4°$

on the centigrade scale of this thermometer. $\checkmark$

6. 1) Heat energy required to raise the temperature of ice from −10 °C to 0 °C,
$Q_1 = mc_i\Delta\theta = 0.10 \times 2100 \times 10 = 2100$ J $\checkmark$

2) Heat energy required to melt the ice,
$Q_2 = ml_i = 0.10 \times 3.25 \times 10^5 = 32\,500$ J $\checkmark$

3) Heat energy required to raise the temperature of water from 0 °C to 100 °C,
$Q_3 = mc_w\Delta\theta = 0.10 \times 4200 \times 100 = 42\,000$ J $\checkmark$

4) Heat energy required to boil the water,
$Q_4 = ml_s = 0.10 \times 2.25 \times 10^6 = 225\,000$ J $\checkmark$
Total heat energy required
$= Q_1 + Q_2 + Q_3 + Q_4 = 301\,600$ J $\checkmark$

8. a) The temperature of the solid rises from 20 °C to 80 °C in 200 s.
The energy supplied by the heater in this time,
$Q = mc\Delta\theta$ where m is the mass of the solid,
$\Delta\theta = 60$ K and $c = 1800$ J kg^{-1} K^{-1}
$\therefore Q = m \times 1800 \times 60 = 108\,000\,m$ $\checkmark$
Since the solid also takes 200 s to melt, the heater must supply an amount of heat energy equal to Q in this time. $\checkmark$
$\therefore$ The specific latent heat of fusion of the substance
$$= \frac{Q}{m} = 108\,000 \text{ J kg}^{-1}$$

b) In the liquid state, the temperature rises from 80 °C to 110 °C in 100 s which is the same rate of rise of temperature as in the solid state. $\checkmark$
The rate of supply of heat energy is the same as before. $\checkmark$
$\therefore$ the specific heat capacity of the liquid is equal to the specific heat capacity of the solid. $\checkmark$
Note: In 100 s, the heater supplies an amount of heat energy equal to 0.5Q. The liquid temperature rises by 30 K in this time.
$\therefore 0.5Q = mc'\Delta\theta$ where $\Delta\theta = 30$ K and c' is the specific heat capacity of the liquid.
$\therefore 0.5 \times 108\,000\,m = mc' \times 30$
Hence $c' = \dfrac{0.5 \times 108\,000}{30} = 1800$ J kg^{-1} K^{-1}

10. Let m_s represent the mass of steam that condenses.
1) Heat energy from the steam when it condenses,
$Q_1 = m_s l_s = m_s \times 2.25 \times 10^6$ J $\checkmark$
2) Heat energy from the condensed steam when it cools from 100 °C to 30 °C,

$Q_2 = m_s c_w \Delta\theta = m_s \times 4200 \times 70$
$\qquad = m_s \times 294\,000$ J ✓

3) Heat energy needed to melt 50 g of ice,
$Q_3 = m_i l_i = 0.050 \times 3.25 \times 10^5 = 16\,250$ J ✓

4) Heat energy needed to heat 250 g of water (= 200 g water originally present +50 g of melted ice) from 0 °C to 30 °C,
$Q_4 = m_w c_w \Delta\theta = 0.250 \times 4200 \times 30$
$\qquad = 31\,500$ J ✓

5) Heat energy needed to heat 120 g of copper from 0 °C to 30 °C,
$Q_5 = m_c c' \Delta\theta = 0.120 \times 380 \times 30 = 1368$ J ✓

Assuming no heat transfer to or from the surroundings,
$Q_1 + Q_2 = Q_3 + Q_4 + Q_5$ ✓
$2.25 \times 10^6 m_s + 2.94 \times 10^5 m_s$
$\qquad = 16\,250 + 31\,500 + 1368$ ✓
$(2.25 + 0.29) \times 10^6 m_s = 49\,118$
$2.54 \times 10^6 m_s = 49\,118$
$m_s = \dfrac{49\,118}{2.54 \times 10^6} = 1.93 \times 10^{-2}$ kg ✓

12. a) Surface area, A_s
$\qquad = 2\pi r L = 2\pi \times 0.35 \times 10^{-3} \times 20$ ✓
$\qquad = 4.40 \times 10^{-2}$ m^2 ✓

b) Using Stefan's law, Power $= \sigma A T^4 = 1000$ W
$\therefore T^4 = \dfrac{1000}{\sigma A_s}$ ✓ $= \dfrac{1000}{5.67 \times 10^{-8} \times 4.40 \times 10^{-2}}$ ✓
$\qquad = 4.00 \times 10^{11}$ K^4
$\therefore T = 796$ K ✓

14. $Q/t = kA \dfrac{(\theta_1 - \theta_2)}{L}$
$\qquad = 0.40 \times 20 \times \dfrac{(10 - 0)}{0.30}$ ✓ $= 267$ W ✓
$\therefore$ heat loss per hour $= 267 \times 3600$
$\qquad = 9.61 \times 10^5$ J h^{-1} ✓

16. Thermal resistance of brick
$\qquad = \dfrac{L}{kA} = \dfrac{0.30}{0.40 \times 20} = 0.0375$ K W^{-1} ✓
Thermal resistance of plaster
$\qquad = \dfrac{L}{kA} = \dfrac{0.010}{0.0040 \times 20} = 0.125$ K W^{-1} ✓
Thermal resistance of brick and plaster
$\qquad = 0.1625$ K W^{-1} ✓
$\therefore$ Heat flow per second
$\qquad = \dfrac{\text{overall temperature difference}}{\text{total thermal resistance}}$
$\qquad = \dfrac{(10 - 0)}{0.1625} = 61.5$ W ✓
$\therefore$ temperature difference across brick = heat flow per second × thermal resistance of the brick
$\qquad = 61.5 \times 0.0375 = 2.3$ K ✓
$\therefore$ temperature of interface $= 2.3$ °C ✓

18. a) For each square metre of surface,
$Q/t = kA \dfrac{(\theta_1 - \theta_2)}{L} = 2.30 \times 1 \times \dfrac{(273 - 263)}{0.010}$ ✓
$\qquad = 2300$ W ✓

b) Consider the thermal energy that needs to be removed to freeze a 1.0 mm layer of water under each square metre of ice.
Volume of water in this layer = thickness × area
$\qquad = 0.0010 \times 1.0 = 0.0010$ m^3. ✓

$\therefore$ Mass of water to be frozen
$\qquad = $ density of water × volume of water
$\qquad = 1000 \times 0.0010 = 1.0$ kg ✓
Thermal energy removed when 1.0 kg of water freezes = mass × specific latent heat of water
$\qquad = 1.0$ kg $\times 3.25 \times 10^5$ J kg$^{-1} = 3.25 \times 10^5$ J ✓
$\therefore$ Time taken to remove 3.25×10^5 J by thermal conduction $= \dfrac{3.25 \times 10^5 \text{ J}}{2300 \text{ W}} = 141$ s ✓
$\therefore$ Rate of growth of ice layer
$\qquad = \dfrac{\text{thickness}}{\text{time taken}} = \dfrac{0.001 \text{ m}}{141 \text{ s}}$ ✓
$\qquad = 7.1 \times 10^{-6}$ m s^{-1} ✓

20. Thermal resistance coefficient of each pane
$\qquad = \dfrac{\text{thickness}}{\text{thermal conductivity}} = \dfrac{0.0040}{1.0}$
$\qquad = 0.0040$ m^2 K W^{-1} ✓

Total thermal resistance coefficient = thermal resistance coefficients for the two panes + the cavity + the internal and external surface resistance coefficients ✓
$\qquad = 2 \times 0.0040 + 0.14 + 0.06 + 0.13$
$\qquad = 0.338$ m^2 K W^{-1} ✓

Thus a surface area of 0.338 m^2 conducts 1 W for a temperature difference of 1 K. The U-value is therefore $\dfrac{1}{0.338} = 2.96$ W m^{-2} K^{-1}. ✓

Chapter 16

2. a) Rearrange $c = f\lambda$ to give
$\lambda = \dfrac{c}{f} = \dfrac{3.0 \times 10^8}{105 \times 10^6}$ ✓ $= 2.86$ m ✓

b) Rearrange $c = f\lambda$ to give
$f = \dfrac{c}{\lambda} = \dfrac{3.0 \times 10^8}{1500}$ ✓ $= 2.0 \times 10^5$ Hz ✓

4. a) At a given position, the amplitude is constant, assuming the student continues to make one end move from side to side. The time period is also constant, assuming the rate at which the rope is made to vibrate is constant.

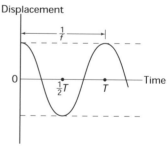

See above for the sketch: ✓ for sinusoidal wave drawn, ✓ for y-axis labelled 'displacement' and x-axis labelled 'time', ✓ for constant amplitude, ✓ for constant time period, ✓ for one cycle on graph marked '1/f'.

b) At a given time, the amplitude decreases with distance along the rope. The wavelength is constant, assuming the rate at which the rope is made to vibrate is constant.

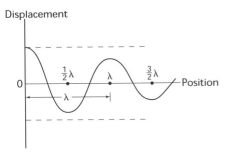

Displacement

See above for the sketch: ✓ for sinusoidal wave drawn, ✓ for *y*-axis labelled 'displacement' and *x*-axis labelled 'distance' or 'position', ✓ for decreasing amplitude, ✓ for constant wavelength, ✓ for one wavelength on graph marked 'wavelength'.

6. The vibrations of a transverse wave are perpendicular to the direction of propagation. ✓ The vibrations of a longitudinal wave are parallel to the direction of propagation.
    a) *Observation*: Place a burning candle near a loudspeaker connected to a signal generator. At low frequency, the sound waves make the candle flame flicker along the direction of propagation of the wave. ✓
       Explanation: The sound wave vibrations make the candle flame spread out along the direction of propagation but not perpendicular to it. ✓
    b) *Observation*: Observe a light bulb through two pieces of polaroid. When one piece of polaroid is rotated relative to the other, the intensity of the transmitted light varies every quarter turn between zero and a maximum. ✓
       Explanation: The light is polarised by the first polaroid it passes through. The second polaroid blocks the light when its molecules are perpendicular to the molecules of the other filter. ✓ Polarisation is a property of transverse waves only. ✓ Therefore light is a transverse wave because it can be polarised. ✓

8. Using Snell's law in the form $\dfrac{\sin i}{\sin r} = \dfrac{c_1}{c_2}$

   gives $\dfrac{\sin 30}{\sin r} = \dfrac{0.10}{0.15}$ ✓

   $\therefore \sin r = \dfrac{0.15}{0.10} \times \sin 30 = 0.75$ ✓

   $\therefore r = 48.6°$ ✓

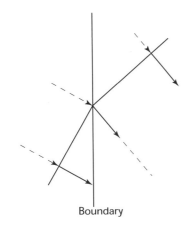

Boundary

See above for the sketch: ✓ ✓ ✓ for correctly drawn wavefront in each part; ✓ for both directions correct.

10. a) See below: ✓ for sketch showing 3 equal loops.

    b) Phase is same as mid-point for every point in the central loop ✓ and 180° out of phase relative to mid-point for every point in the outer two loops. ✓
    c) Wavelength $= \dfrac{2L}{3} = \dfrac{2}{3} \times 1.5 = 1.0$ m. ✓
       Wave speed = wavelength × frequency
       $= 1.0$ m $\times 85$ Hz $= 85$ m s^{-1} ✓

12. a) Distance $= 10x$ ✓
       $\therefore$ Time taken $= \dfrac{\text{distance}}{\text{speed}}$ ✓ $= \dfrac{10x}{x \,(k/m)^{1/2}}$
       $= 10 \,(m/k)^{1/2}$
       $= 10 \times (0.8/25)^{1/2} = 1.79$ s ✓
    b) (i) Volume of each atom $= x^3$ ✓
       Density $\rho = \dfrac{\text{mass}}{\text{volume}} = \dfrac{m}{x^3}$ ✓
       (ii) Wave speed $= x(k/m)^{1/2} = x(k/\rho x^3)^{1/2}$ ✓
       $= (k/\rho x)^{1/2}$ ✓
       (iii) When the spacing between two atoms is increased by extension *e*, the force due to that atom $= ke$, acting over an area x^2. ✓
       $\therefore$ stress $= \dfrac{\text{tension}}{\text{area}} = \dfrac{ke}{x^2}$ ✓
       Also, strain $= \dfrac{\text{extension}}{\text{length}} = \dfrac{e}{x}$ ✓
       Young modulus, $E = \dfrac{\text{stress}}{\text{strain}} = \dfrac{ke}{x^2} \div \dfrac{e}{x} = \dfrac{k}{x}$ ✓
       $\therefore k = Ex$
       $\therefore$ Wave speed $c = (k/\rho x)^{1/2}$
       $= (Ex/\rho x)^{1/2}$ ✓ $= (E/\rho)^{1/2}$ ✓
       (iv) $c = (E/\rho)^{1/2} = (0.7 \times 10^{11}/2700)^{1/2}$ ✓
       $= 5090$ m s^{-1} ✓

Chapter 22

2. Rearrange $I = nvAq$ to give $v = \dfrac{I}{nAq}$ ✓

   where the area of cross-section $A = \dfrac{\pi d^2}{4}$ and

   $q = 1.6 \times 10^{-19}$ C

   Area of cross-section $= \dfrac{\pi d^2}{4}$

   $= \dfrac{\pi \times (0.40 \times 10^{-3})^2}{4}$ ✓ $= 1.26 \times 10^{-7}$ m^2 ✓

   $\therefore v = \dfrac{I}{nAq} = \dfrac{5.0}{1.0 \times 10^{29} \times 1.26 \times 10^{-7} \times 1.6 \times 10^{-19}}$ ✓

   $= 2.49 \times 10^{-3}$ m s^{-1} ✓

4. $Q = It = 1.0 \times (20 \times 60 \times 60) = 7.2 \times 10^4$ C ✓
   $E = QV = 7.2 \times 10^4 \times 12 = 8.64 \times 10^5$ J ✓

6. a) See diagram below: ✓ for correct symbols,
    ✓ components in series.

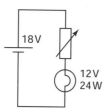

b) Rearrange $P = IV$ to give

$I = \dfrac{P}{V}$ ✓ $= \dfrac{24}{12} = 2.0$ A ✓

$R = \dfrac{V}{I} = \dfrac{12}{2.0} = 6.0 \, \Omega$ ✓

c) P.d. across variable resistor
    = battery p.d. – p.d. across X ✓
    = 18 – 12 = 6.0 V ✓
    Power dissipated in variable resistor
    = current × p.d. across variable resistor
    = 2.0 × 6.0 = 12.0 W ✓

8. See diagram below for the circuit diagram. ✓

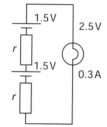

a) Total e.m.f. $\varepsilon = 2 \times 1.5$ V = 3.0 V ✓
    $\varepsilon = IR + Ir$, where IR = p.d. across the
    torchbulb = 2.5 V and Ir = lost p.d. due to total
    internal resistance r. ✓
    $\therefore Ir = \varepsilon - IR = 3.0 - 2.5 = 0.5$ V. ✓
    Since $I = 0.3$ A, then $r = \dfrac{Ir}{I} = \dfrac{0.5}{0.3} = 1.67 \, \Omega$ for
    both cells ✓
    $\therefore$ Internal resistance of each cell = 0.83 Ω ✓
b) Electrical power supplied by cells
    = current × total e.m.f.
    = 0.3 × 3.0 = 0.9 W ✓
c) Power delivered to the torchbulb
    = current × p.d. across the torchbulb
    = 0.3 × 2.5 = 0.75 W ✓
    The difference of 0.15 W is due to power
    wasted inside the cells due to internal
    resistance. ✓

10. Circuit A only
a) Resistance of 4 Ω and 12 Ω in parallel = R_1

    where $\dfrac{1}{R_1} = \dfrac{1}{4} + \dfrac{1}{12} = \dfrac{12 + 4}{4 \times 12} = \dfrac{16}{48}$ ✓

    $\therefore R_1 = \dfrac{48}{16} = 3.0 \, \Omega$ ✓

    $\therefore$ Total resistance $R = 3.0 + R_1 = 6.0 \, \Omega$ ✓

b) Cell current $I = \dfrac{\text{cell e.m.f.}}{R}$ ✓ $= \dfrac{6.0}{6.0} = 1.0$ A ✓

c) **3Ω resistor:**
    current = 1.0 A (= battery current as the battery
    and the 3 ohm resistor are in series). ✓
    p.d. across resistor = current × resistance
    = 1.0 × 3.0 = 3.0 V ✓

power = p.d. × current = 3.0 × 1.0 = 3.0 W ✓
4Ω resistor:
p.d. across 4 ohm resistor
    = cell e.m.f. – p.d. across 3 ohm resistor
    = 6.0 – 3.0 = 3.0 V ✓
current = $\dfrac{\text{p.d.}}{\text{resistance}} = \dfrac{3.0}{4.0} = 0.75$ A ✓
power = p.d. × current = 3.0 × 0.75
    = 2.25 W ✓
12Ω resistor:
p.d. across 12 ohm resistor
    = cell e.m.f. – p.d. across 3 ohm resistor
    = 6.0 – 3.0 = 3.0 V ✓
current = $\dfrac{\text{p.d.}}{\text{resistance}} = \dfrac{3.0}{12.0} = 0.25$ A ✓
*Note: cell current = current through 4 ohm
resistor + current through 12 ohm resistor.*
power = p.d. × current = 3.0 × 0.25
    = 0.75 W ✓
d) Electrical power delivered by cell
    = cell current × cell e.m.f.
    = 1.0 × 6 = 6.0 W
*Note: Power delivered to
resistors = 3.0 W + 2.25 W + 0.75 W = 6.0 W as
above.*

12. Use the following answers from Q22.9 for this
    question:
    e.m.f. of cell = 1.37 V, internal resistance = 1.14 Ω
    The new circuit diagram is shown in the diagram
    below.

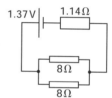

a) The combined resistance of two 8 Ω resistors in
    parallel = 4.0 Ω $(= (1/8 + 1/8)^{-1})$ ✓
    $\therefore$ the total resistance = 4 + 1.14 = 5.14 Ω ✓
    Current from cell = $\dfrac{\text{cell e.m.f.}}{\text{total resistance}}$

    $= \dfrac{1.37}{5.14} = 0.267$ A ✓

    $\therefore$ Current through each 8 ohm resistor
    = 0.133 A ✓

14. a) See diagram below for the graph: ✓ for correct
    plotting of points, ✓ for correct curve, ✓ for

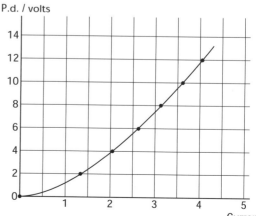

correct labels on axes, ✓ for appropriate scales (points to cover at least half of each axis).

b) Read the p.d. off the graph for each value of current then calculate the resistance using

$$R = \frac{V}{I}$$

(i) $V = 1.5$ V, $R = 1.5\ \Omega$ ✓
(ii) $V = 3.4$ V, $R = 1.7\ \Omega$ ✓
(iii) $V = 11.6$ V, $R = 2.95\ \Omega$ ✓

16. Rearrange $R = \dfrac{\rho L}{A}$ to give $\dfrac{R}{L} = \dfrac{\rho}{A}$ ✓

Area of cross-section $= \dfrac{\pi d^2}{4} = \dfrac{\pi \times (0.35 \times 10^{-3})^2}{4}$ ✓

$= 9.62 \times 10^{-8}\ \text{m}^2$ ✓

$\dfrac{R}{L} = \dfrac{\rho}{A} = \dfrac{4.8 \times 10^{-7}}{9.62 \times 10^{-8}} = 5.0\ \Omega\ \text{m}^{-1}$ ✓

18. See the diagram below for the circuit diagram:
✓ for correct polarity, ✓ for correct connection of 2.0 ohm resistor.

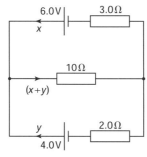

Let current through 6 V cell $= x$ and let the current through the 4 V cell $= y$.

a) Applying Kirchhoff's second law to the circuit loop containing the 6.0 V cell only gives:
$6.0 = 3x + 10(x + y)$ ✓
$\therefore 6.0 = 13x + 10y$ ✓

Applying Kirchhoff's second law to the circuit loop containing the 4.0 V cell only gives:
$4.0 = 2y + 10(x + y)$ ✓
$\therefore 4.0 = 10x + 12y$ ✓

Multiply the first equation by 10 and the second equation by 13 and subtract the second equation from the first equation, to give:
$\therefore 60 - 52 = 130x + 100y - 130x - 156y$
$\therefore 8 = -56y$ ✓

$\therefore y = -\dfrac{8}{56} = -0.14$ A ✓

$10x = 4.0 - 12y = 5.71$

$x = \dfrac{5.71}{10} = 0.57$ A ✓

b) Resistor current $= x + y = 0.57 - 0.14 = 0.43$ A ✓
c) P.d. across 10 ohm resistor
$= \text{current} \times \text{resistance}$
$= 0.43 \times 10 = 4.3$ V ✓

20. Kettle: $3.0 \times 0.50 = 1.5$ kW h,
TV $= 0.5 \times 3 = 1.5$ kW h
Cooker $= 6 \times 2 = 12$ kW h,
Light bulb $= 0.100 \times 5 = 0.5$ kW h
✓✓ for all correct, ✓ for three only correct.
$\therefore$ total number of units used $= 15.5$ kW h ✓
Cost $= 15.5 \times 5p = 77.5p$ ✓

Capacitors in d.c. circuits

22. a) (i) $Q = CV = 2.2 \times 10^{-6} \times 9.0 = 1.92 \times 10^{-5}$ C ✓
(ii) $E = \frac{1}{2} CV^2 = 0.5 \times 2.2 \times 10^{-6} \times 9.0^2$
$= 8.9 \times 10^{-5}$ J ✓

b) Energy supplied by battery $= QV = CV^2$
$= 2.2 \times 10^{-6} \times 9.0^2 = 1.78 \times 10^{-4}$ J ✓

c) Energy supplied to the capacitor $= \frac{1}{2} QV$
$(= \frac{1}{2} CV^2)$
Energy supplied by battery $= QV$
Difference is energy dissipated in the wires due to resistance. ✓

24. a) See figure below for the circuit diagram. ✓

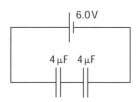

(i) Let $C_T =$ the combined capacitance:
$\dfrac{1}{C_T} = \dfrac{1}{4} + \dfrac{1}{4} = \dfrac{1}{2}$ $\therefore C_T = 2\ \mu$F ✓
P.d. across each capacitor, $V = 3.0$ V ✓

$\therefore$ Energy stored in each capacitor
$= \dfrac{1}{2} CV^2 = 0.5 \times 4.0 \times 10^{-6} \times 3.0^2$
$= 1.8 \times 10^{-5}$ J ✓

(ii) Energy supplied by the battery $= QV_{\text{batt}}$ ✓
$= C_T V_{batt}^2 = 2.0 \times 10^{-6} \times 6.0^2 = 7.2 \times 10^{-5}$ J ✓

b) See figure below for the circuit diagram. ✓

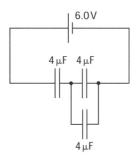

(i) The combined capacitance of the two capacitors in parallel $= 4 + 4 = 8\ \mu$F ✓
The total capacitance,
$C_0 = \left(\dfrac{1}{8} + \dfrac{1}{4}\right)^{-1} = \dfrac{32}{12} = 2.67\ \mu$F ✓
Total charge stored, Q
$= C_0 V_{batt} = 2.67 \times 10^{-6} \times 6.0$
$= 1.6 \times 10^{-5}$ C ✓

4 μF capacitor in series with the cell:
Charge stored $= Q = 1.6 \times 10^{-5}$ C ✓
P.d. across capacitor, V
$= \dfrac{Q}{C} = \dfrac{1.6 \times 10^{-5}}{4.0 \times 10^{-6}} = 4.0$ V ✓
Energy stored $= \frac{1}{2} QV = 0.5 \times 1.6 \times 10^{-5} \times 4.0$
$= 3.2 \times 10^{-5}$ J ✓

4µF capacitor in parallel with each other:
Charge stored = $0.5Q = 8.0 \times 10^{-6}$ C (in each) ✓✓

P.d. across capacitor,

$$V = \frac{Q}{C} = \frac{8.0 \times 10^{-6}}{4.0 \times 10^{-6}} = 2.0 \text{ V} \quad ✓$$

Energy stored
$$= \tfrac{1}{2}QV = 0.5 \times 8.0 \times 10^{-6} \times 2.0 = 8.0 \times 10^{-6} \text{ J}$$
(in each) ✓✓

ii) Energy supplied by battery = QV_{batt}
$$= 1.6 \times 10^{-5} \times 6 = 9.6 \times 10^{-5} \text{ J} \quad ✓$$

∴ additional energy stored
$$= 9.6 \times 10^{-5} - 7.2 \times 10^{-5} = 2.4 \times 10^{-5} \text{ J} \quad ✓$$

26. The p.d. across a capacitor must not exceed 6 V, therefore two capacitors in series across battery would be at the maximum working voltage. The diagram below shows 3 pairs of capacitors in series connected in parallel with each other across a 12 V battery. ✓✓

Any other combination would store less charge as there would be more than two capacitors in series so the p.d. across any capacitor would be less than 6 V and the charge stored would be less than in the figure below.

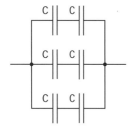

In the figure above, the combined capacitance of two capacitors in series = 0.5 C, where C is the capacitance of a single capacitor. ✓

∴ the total capacitance = $3 \times 0.5C$
$$= 1.5 \times 100 \text{ µF} = 150 \text{ µF} \quad ✓$$

∴ Total charge stored
= total capacitance × battery p.d.
$$= 150 \times 10^{-6} \times 6 = 9.0 \times 10^{-4} \text{ J} \quad ✓$$

Total energy stored
$$= \tfrac{1}{2} \times \text{total capacitance} \times \text{battery p.d.}^2$$
$$= 0.5 \times 150 \times 10^{-6} \times 6^2 = 2.7 \times 10^{-3} \text{ J} \quad ✓$$

28. The circuit is shown in the figure below.

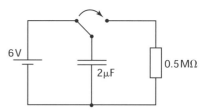

a) Energy stored = $\tfrac{1}{2}CV^2 = 0.5 \times 2.0 \times 10^{-6} \times 6.0^2$
$$= 3.6 \times 10^{-5} \text{J} ✓$$

b) Initial discharge current
$$I_0 = \frac{V_{batt}}{R} = \frac{6}{0.5 \times 10^6} = 12 \text{ µA} \quad ✓$$

c) $RC = 0.5 \times 10^6 \times 2 \times 10^{-6} = 1$ s ✓
$$V = V_0 e^{-t/RC} = 6.0 e^{-1/1} = 6.0 \times 0.368 = 2.21 \text{ V} \quad ✓$$

30. a) Energy stored = $\tfrac{1}{2}CV^2$
$$= 0.5 \times 4700 \times 10^{-6} \times 10.0^2 = 0.235 \text{ J} \quad ✓$$

b) Work done = $mgh = 0.1 \times 0.12 = 0.012$ J ✓

c) Efficiency = $\dfrac{\text{work done}}{\text{energy stored}} = \dfrac{0.012}{0.235} = 0.051$ ✓

The difference is energy dissipated due to resistance of the wires, friction, noise etc. ✓

4 | Essential mathematics

 Basic mathematics

Indices

Raising to a power is a common operation in calculations. For example $5 \times 5 \times 5$ is stated as '5 to the power 3' and written 5^3. In this example, 3 is the **index** and 5 is the **base**. Powers of ten are used to simplify very large or very small numbers. The **standard form** used for expressing any number, is as a number between 1 and 10 multiplied by the appropriate power of ten. It saves writing long strings of zeros. For example, the speed of light is equal to 3.0×10^8 m s^{-1}; written as 300 000 000 m s^{-1}, it is less than convenient. Try writing the value of the electronic charge (= 1.6×10^{-19} C) in non-standard form! The power of ten indicates how many decimal places the decimal point is to be moved to convert the number to standard form. The sign of the index is important too, since it gives the direction the point is to be moved.

$\frac{1}{10\,000}$	$\frac{1}{1000}$	$\frac{1}{100}$	$\frac{1}{10}$	1	10	100	1000	10 000
10^{-4}	10^{-3}	10^{-2}	10^{-1}	10^{0}	10^{1}	10^{2}	10^{3}	10^{4}

Finding the roots of a number is the inverse of 'raising to a power'. For example, $3^2 = 9$ is where 3 is raised to the power 2. So the inverse operation is $9^{1/2} = \sqrt{9} = 3$. In other words, the square root of 9 is 3. The $\sqrt{\ }$ sign must be used carefully because it is usually taken to mean the square root (i.e. power = $\frac{1}{2}$) unless the sign is accompanied by a small number placed in the 'hook'. The cube root of 8 is written $8^{1/3}$ or $\sqrt[3]{8}$ which is equal to 2.

Suppose a number in standard form is to be raised to a given power. For example, suppose we wish to calculate

$$(3.4 \times 10^6)^3 = (3.4)^3 \times (10^6)^3$$

$$= (3.4 \times 3.4 \times 3.4) \times (10^6 \times 10^6 \times 10^6)$$

$$= 39.304 \times 10^{18} = 3.9304 \times 10^{19}.$$

The cube of 10^6 is $(10^6)^3 = 10^{6 \times 3} = 10^{18}$; the two powers are multiplied together.

The same rule applies to roots of numbers in standard form. For example, the fourth root of (2.64×10^8) is written as $(2.64 \times 10^8)^{1/4}$ which equals $2.64^{1/4} \times (10^8)^{1/4}$.
Since $2.64^{1/4} = 1.2747$ and $(10^8)^{1/4} = 10^2$, then the final answer is 1.2747×10^2.

Multiplying or dividing numbers in standard form involves separating the 'power of ten' part from the rest of the number. Consider the following example.

Calculate the value of $\dfrac{(1.6 \times 10^{-19}) \times (2.0 \times 10^3)}{9.1 \times 10^{-31}}$

Separating the powers of ten gives

$$\left(\frac{1.6 \times 2.0}{9.1}\right) \times \left(\frac{10^{-19} \times 10^3}{10^{-31}}\right) = 0.3516 \times 10^{-19+3-(-31)}$$

Handling powers of ten is an important part of calculation skills. The longer method for the above example is not just tedious but liable to error.

$$10^{-19} \times \frac{10^3}{10^{-31}}$$

$$= \frac{0.000\,000\,000\,000\,000\,000\,1 \times 1000}{0.000\,000\,000\,000\,000\,000\,000\,000\,000\,000\,000\,1}$$

$$= \frac{1000}{0.000\,000\,000\,001} = 10^{15}$$

The example shows the advantages of being able to handle powers of ten; the rules are based on moving the decimal point according to the indices.

$$10^a \times 10^b = 10^{a+b}$$

$$\frac{10^a}{10^b} = 10^a \times 10^{-b} = 10^{a-b}$$

Significant figures reflect the accuracy of a number. The number of significant figures of a numerical value is the number of digits except for zeros at the beginning. For example, the number 0.034 05 has four significant figures; 21 540 has 5. The number of significant figures which any numerical value is allowed must be consistent with the accuracy of the value. For example, suppose you wish to determine the average speed of a falling object by timing it as it falls through a measured vertical distance.

Distance fallen = 5.00 m

Time taken = 1.05 s

Average speed = $\dfrac{\text{distance}}{\text{time taken}}$

$$= \frac{5.00}{1.05} = 4.761\,905 \text{ m s}^{-1}$$

using a calculator. But the measurements cannot justify all the figures in the answer from the calculator. So we must round-off the value to the number of significant figures that can be justified. For example, if the measurements justify two significant figures only, then the average speed is written as 4.8 m s^{-1}. Note that the next significant figure is rounded down if it is less than 5, and rounded up if it is 5 or more.

6.325 641 becomes 6.33 to 3 sig. fig.
0.001 527 becomes 0.001 53 to 3 sig. fig.
100.95 becomes 101 to 3 sig. fig.

Calculations

Using a calculator gives the wrong answer very easily unless you know how to use the calculator correctly. Different types of calculator have different rules for use so you must learn to use your own calculator effectively. Raising to a power can present problems using an unfamiliar calculator. Some guidelines for using calculators are listed below.

- Don't hurry because it is all too easy to bounce a key twice by mistake or to press the wrong key.
- For a lengthy calculation, work through in stages and write the values down at the end of each stage. Using the memory facility of a calculator can cause errors if you forget to clear the memory first.
- Write the answer down in standard form. Take care not to write any power of ten on the display as a power of the number. For example, if the display shows '5.6 13', then you write down 5.6×10^{13} *not* 5.6^{13} which is very different.

WORKED EXAMPLE

Calculate the density of a spherical ball bearing from the following measurements.
mass $m = 4.85 \times 10^{-3}$ kg,
diameter $d = 1.05 \times 10^{-2}$ m.

Solution
<u>STEP 1</u> The volume V of the ball bearing $= \frac{4}{3}\pi(d/2)^3$
Hence $V = \frac{4}{3}\pi(0.525 \times 10^{-2})^3$
$= \frac{4}{3}\pi \times (0.525)^3 \times 10^{-2 \times 3}$
So $V = 0.606 \times 10^{-6}$ m^3
<u>STEP 2</u> Write down the value for V from your calculator.
<u>STEP 3</u> Calculate the density $\rho =$ mass/volume.

$$\rho = \frac{4.85 \times 10^{-2}}{0.606 \times 10^{-6}} = 8000 \text{ kg m}^{-3}$$

Using tables for calculations is perhaps a skill not much needed now. But if your calculator develops a fault, then you may be forced to call on your skill in this area. Tables are available for **reciprocals** (i.e. $1/a$ is the reciprocal of a), squares, square roots and much more. The most useful are **logarithms**

because they can be used in place of the other tables if you know the basic rules. The two important types of log tables are

- base 10 logs, written as $\log_{10}$ or simply lg,
- natural logs, written as $\log_e$ or just ln.

The logarithm in a given base of any number is the power the base must be raised to in order to equal the number. For example $\log_{10} 1000$ equals 3 because $10^3 = 1000$.

Multiplication using logs
If $a = 10^x$ where a is any positive number, then $x = \log_{10} a$ and if $b = 10^y$ where b is any positive number, then $y = \log_{10} b$.
Therefore $a \times b = 10^x \times 10^y = 10^{x+y}$, so
$x + y = \log_{10}(ab)$

Hence $\log_{10}(ab) = \log_{10} a + \log_{10} b$

WORKED EXAMPLE

$a = 6.512$, $b = 0.3649$.
Calculate $c = ab$.

Solution
$\log_{10} a = 0.8137$
$\log_{10} b = -1 + 0.5621 = -0.4378$
(since $\log_{10} 0.3649 = \log_{10}\ 3.649/10$
$= \log_{10} 3.649 - \log_{10} 10 = 0.5621 - 1$)
Hence $\log_{10} ab = \log_{10} a + \log_{10} b$
$= 0.8137 - 0.4378 = 0.3759$

Now look up the antilog of 0.3759.
In other words, what number has its $\log_{10}$ equal to 0.3759? A look at Fig 4.1 shows that the answer is 2.376.
So $ab = 2.376$.

Division by logs
If $a = 10^x$, then $x = \log_{10} a$. If $b = 10^y$, then $y = \log_{10} b$, so $a/b = 10^x/10^y = 10^{x-y}$.
Hence $x - y = \log_{10}(a/b) = \log_{10} a - \log_{10} b$

$\log_{10}(a/b) = \log_{10} a - \log_{10} b$

WORKED EXAMPLE

$a = 2.658$, $b = 34.23$
Calculate a/b.

Solution
$\log_{10} a = 0.4245$
$\log_{10} b = 1.5344$
(since $\log_{10} 34.23 + \log_{10}(10 \times 3.423)$
$= \log_{10} 10 + \log_{10} 3.423 = 1 + 0.5344$)

Number	0	1	2	3	4	5	6	7	8	9
2.3	.3617	.3636	.3655	.3674	.3692	.3711	.3729	.3747	.3766	.3784

$\log_{10} 2.376 = 0.3759$

Fig 4.1 Using log tables

Hence $\log_{10}(a/b) = \log_{10} a - \log_{10} b = -1.1098$
To determine the antilog of this number using tables, it must be written as $-2 + 0.8901$ (or $\bar{2}.8901$). The antilog of 0.8901 is 7.764, and the '-2' (or $\bar{2}$) tells us to move the decimal point two places to the left. So the answer is 0.077 64.
$a/b = 0.077\ 64$
A quick way to set out this calculation is shown below:
$a = 2.658$
$b = 34.23$
Calculate a/b using log tables.

Number	log
$a = 2.658$	0.4245
$b = 34.23$	1.5344
a/b	$\bar{2}.8901$

$a/b = 7.764 \times 10^{-2} = 0.07764$
Note: $\bar{2}.8901$ means $-2 + 0.8901$
The $\bar{2}$ tells you to move the decimal point of 7.764 two places to the left.

Using logs to raise a number to a given power

Suppose we wish to raise n to a given power p (i.e. calculate n^p).
Let $x = n^p$, then $\log x = \log n^p = p \log n$.
So x is equal to the number whose log is $p \log n$. The reason why $\log n^p$ equals $p \log n$ is that

$$\log n^p = \log (n \times n \times \overset{p\ times}{\cdots\cdots\cdots} \times n)$$
$$= \log n + \log n + \ldots + \log n$$
$$= p \log n.$$

WORKED EXAMPLE

Find $6^{1.4}$.

Solution
If $x = 6^{1.4}$, then $\log_{10} x = 1.4 \log_{10} 6$
$= 1.4 \times 0.7781 = 1.089\ 41$.
The antilog of 1.0894 is 12.29; this is because the antilog of 0.0894 is 1.229 and the '1' in front of the decimal point tells us to move the point one place to the right. Hence $x = 12.29$.

Using logs to find a given root of a number

The root is written as a fraction. So the fifth root of 6 is written $6^{1/5}$. Then the same procedure as in the previous example is used.

WORKED EXAMPLE

Find $6^{1/5}$.

Solution

Let $x = 6^{1/5}$, so $\log_{10} x = (1/5) \times \log_{10} 6$
$= 0.7781/5 = 0.1556$.

The antilog of this number is 1.4309.
Hence $x = 1.4309$.

In the above examples, base 10 logs have been used. Natural logs could have been used although you can easily make an error in 'moving the decimal point'. Try some calculations using base 10 logs, and check your answers with a calculator. Then, you have a fall back if your calculator lets you down in an examination.

Trigonometry

Angles are measured in degrees or radians. The symbol for the radian is rad. The scale for conversion is 360 degrees = 2π radians, so 1 rad = $360/2\pi$ degrees.

The circumference of a circle of radius $r = 2\pi r$, so the circumference can be written as $r \times$ the angle in radians round the circle.

For a segment of a circle, the length of the arc of the segment is in proportion to the angle θ subtended by the arc to the centre. Since the angle 2π radians corresponds to an arc length equal to the circumference ($2\pi r$), then $\dfrac{\theta}{2\pi} = \dfrac{\text{arc length } s}{\text{circumference } 2\pi r}$

So $\theta = \dfrac{s}{r}$ (See Fig 4.2)

Giving $s = r\theta$
where $s =$ arc length,
$r =$ radius,
$\theta =$ angle in radians.

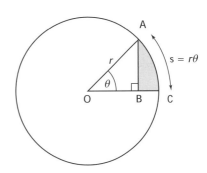

Fig 4.2 Segments and triangles

The right-angled triangle is used to define sines, cosines and tangents. Figure 4.3 shows a right-angled triangle XYZ in which side XY is the hypotenuse (i.e. the side opposite the right angle), YZ is opposite to angle θ ($=\hat{XYZ}$) and XZ is adjacent to angle θ.

$$\sin \theta = \frac{YZ}{XY} = \frac{o}{h}$$
$$\cos \theta = \frac{XZ}{XY} = \frac{a}{h}$$
$$\tan \theta = \frac{YZ}{XZ} = \frac{o}{a}$$

where o = side opposite to θ (i.e. YZ)

h = hypotenuse,

a = side adjacent to θ (i.e. XZ).

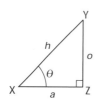

Fig 4.3 The right-angled triangle

Graphs of $\sin \theta$ and $\cos \theta$ against θ are shown in Fig 4.4. The maximum value of $\sin \theta$ is 1 which is when $\theta = 90° = \pi/2$ radians. At this angle YZ = XY and XZ = 0 so $\sin \theta = 1$.

The maximum value of $\cos \theta$ is when $\theta = 0$; here YZ = 0 so XZ = XY hence $\cos \theta = 1$ at $\theta = 0$.

The value of $\tan \theta$ is 0 when $\theta = 0$ because YZ is zero at $\theta = 0$. When $\theta = 45°$, YZ = XZ so $\tan 45° = 1$. As θ approaches 90°, XZ tends to zero as YZ tends to 1; so $\tan \theta$ tends to infinity at 90°.

$$\tan \theta = \frac{o}{a} = \frac{o}{h} \div \frac{a}{h} = \frac{\sin \theta}{\cos \theta}$$

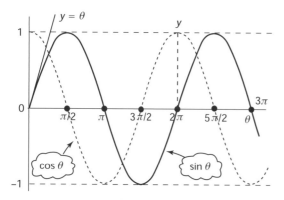

Fig 4.4 Sine and cosine curves

Pythagoras' theorem gives a useful link between $\sin \theta$ and $\cos \theta$. From Fig 4.3, Pythagoras' theorem can be written

$$YZ^2 + XZ^2 = XY^2$$

$$o^2 + a^2 = h^2$$

$$\text{So} \left(\frac{o}{h}\right)^2 + \left(\frac{a}{h}\right)^2 = 1$$

Hence $\sin^2 \theta + \cos^2 \theta = 1$

The small angle approximation for $\sin \theta$ is used in lots of topics in physics. The approximation is sometimes called the 'skinny triangle' rule. Figure 4.2 shows a triangle OAB which is part of segment OAC of a circle. The length of the arc from

A to C is greater than the distance AB along the straight line.

Arc length $s = r\theta$

Straight line distance $x = r \sin \theta$.

Now suppose we make angle θ much smaller so the situation is like Fig 4.5. So the triangle OAB becomes 'skinny'; now the arc length AC is virtually the same as the straight line distance AB. So $r \sin \theta$ is approximately equal to $r\theta$ for small angles.

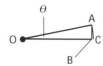

Fig 4.5 $\sin \theta \approx \theta$

$\sin \theta = \theta$ (in radians)

for angles less than about 10°.

Figure 4.4 shows the line $y = \theta$ on the graph of the sine wave; up to about 10°, the sine wave is virtually straight and follows the line $\sin \theta = \theta$.

The cosine wave shows that $\cos \theta$ is approximately 1 for small angles; Fig 4.5 shows that OA is approximately equal to OB for small angles AOB.

So $\cos \theta = $ OB/OA is approximately equal to 1 here.

 Mathematical links

Signs and symbols

Symbols used in equations and formulae represent physical variables. Any physical variable has a magnitude and a unit. So a symbol represents a number *and* a unit. The number is meaningless without the unit. If you received a bill that stated 'Amount owing = 77' you would be puzzled because no unit is given. So the unit, (£ or p in this case), is essential. The same applies to any physical variable; an instruction to move a lens holder by a distance of 30 is meaningless because you do not know whether 30 mm or 30 cm is intended. The same applies when you give answers to numerical problems; give the unit or else your answer is meaningless.

Inequality signs are often used in physics. You need to be able to recognize the meaning of the signs in the table at the top of the next page.

The approximation sign is used where an estimate or an order-of-magnitude calculation is made rather than an accurate calculation. For an order-of-magnitude calculation, the final value is written with one significant figure only or even rounded up or down to the nearest power of ten. For example, the order-of-magnitude value of the Earth's mass is 10^{25} kg although a more exact value is 6×10^{24} kg. Order-of-magnitude calculations are useful as a

Sign	Meaning	Example of use	Meaning of example
>	greater than	$T > 300$ K	T is greater than 300 K
<	less than	$T < 300$ K	T is less than 300 K
⩾	greater than or equal to	$T \geqslant 300$ K	T is greater than or equal to 300 K
⩽	less than or equal to	$T \leqslant 300$ K	T is less than or equal to 300 K
≫	much greater than	$T \gg 300$ K	T is much greater than 300 K
≪	much less than	$T \ll 300$ K	T is much less than 300 K
≈	approximately equals	$T \approx 300$ K	T is about 300 K

quick check after using a calculator. For example, if you are asked to calculate the density of a 1.0 kg metal cylinder of height 0.100 m and diameter 0.071 m, you ought to obtain a value of 2530 kg m^{-3} using a calculator. Now let's check the value.

$$\text{Volume} = \pi\,(\text{radius})^2 \times \text{height}$$
$$\approx 3 \times (0.04)^2 \times 0.1 \approx 48 \times 10^{-5}\ \text{m}^3$$
$$\text{Density} = \text{mass/volume}$$
$$\approx 1.0/50 \times 10^{-5} \approx 2000\ \text{kg m}^{-3}$$

(This 'confirms' our accurate calculation.)

Proportionality is represented by the $\propto$ sign. A simple example of its use in physics is for Hooke's law; the tension in a spring is proportional to its extension.

tension $T \propto$ extension x

By introducing a constant of proportionality k the link above can be made into an equation.

$T = kx$

where k is defined as the 'spring constant'.

With any proportionality relationship, if one of the variables is increased by a given factor (e.g. ×3), the other variable is increased by the same factor. So in the above example, if T is trebled then extension x is also trebled.

Straight line graphs

Links between two physical quantities can be established most easily by graph plotting. One of the physical quantities is represented by the vertical scale (the 'ordinate', often called the y-axis) and the other quantity by the horizontal scale (the 'abscissa', often called the x-axis). The simplest link is where the plotted points define a straight line. For example, Fig 4.6 shows the link between the tension and the extension of a spring; the gradient of the line is constant and the line passes through the origin. Any situation where the y-variable is proportional to the x-variable gives a straight line

through the origin. For Fig 4.6, the gradient of the line is equal to the spring constant k.

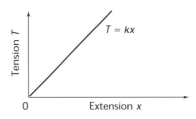

Fig 4.6 Graph links

The general equation for a straight line graph is usually written in the form

$$y = mx + c$$

where m = gradient,

c = y-intercept (i.e. where $x = 0$ and $y = c$).

Figure 4.7 shows several straight lines.
- Line A: $c = 0$ so the line passes through the origin; its equation is $y = 2x$.
- Line B: $m > 0$ so the line has a positive gradient; its equation is $y = 2x - 2$.

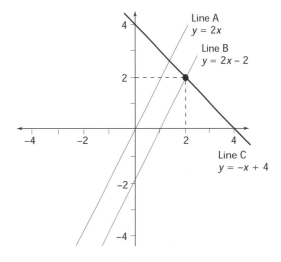

Fig 4.7 Straight line graphs

- Line C: $m < 0$ so the line has a negative gradient; its equation is $y = -x + 4$.

Simultaneous equations can be solved graphically by plotting the line for each equation. The solution of the equations is given by the coordinates of the point(s) where the lines meet. For example, Fig 4.7 shows that lines B and C meet at a single point, $(x = 2, y = 2)$. These coordinates are the only ones to fit both equations.

Solving simultaneous equations doesn't require graph plotting if the equations can be arranged to eliminate one of the variables. Let's use the same example as above.

Line B: $y = 2x - 2$
Line C: $y = -x + 4$

At the point where they meet, their y-coordinates are equal so

$2x - 2 = -x + 4$.

Hence the x-coordinate at the meeting point is given by

$3x = 6$ so $x = 2$.

Since $y = 2x - 2$, then $y = 2 \times 2 - 2$ so $y = 2$.

In physics, simultaneous equations are used to solve circuit equations for currents.

Using Graphs

To test a known link between two physical quantities, use the theory to give a straight line. For example, suppose you are asked to test Boyle's law, that pressure × volume is constant at constant temperature for a particular gas at a certain temperature. The measurements give a set of values of pressure and volume. A graph of pressure against volume (see Fig 4.8) does little to show if the pressure × volume is indeed constant for this particular gas. The equation linking pressure p and volume V for a gas that does obey Boyle's law is

$pV = \text{constant}$

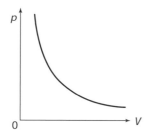

Fig 4.8 p against V for an ideal gas

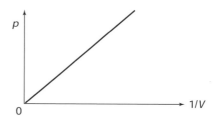

Fig 4.9 p against $1/V$ for an ideal gas

For a straight line graph (see Fig 4.9) rearrange the equation to make p the subject.

$p = \text{constant}/V$

So by plotting a graph of pressure against 1/volume, if the points define a straight line, then the gas does obey Boyle's law.

The same idea applies in many other situations for which we wish to test the validity of an equation; make one of the variables the subject of the equation and plot accordingly. Consider the example of the simple pendulum, which uses the time period (T) and the length (L) to measure the acceleration due to gravity (g).

Time period $T = 2\pi\sqrt{L/g}$

where L is the length of the pendulum.

Measurements would give a set of values for T and L, but a graph of T against L would be of little help. Far more useful would be either a graph of T against $\sqrt{L}$ or T^2 against L, which ought to give a straight line. For T against $\sqrt{L}$, the gradient is $2\pi/\sqrt{g}$; for T against L^2 the gradient is $4\pi^2/g$.

To establish a link between two physical quantities, a log–log graph can be helpful. Suppose two quantities, Y and X, are linked by an equation of the form

$Y = kX^n$

where k is a constant and n is a power to be determined.

$\log Y = \log k + \log X^n$
so $\log Y = \log k + n \log X$
since $\log X^n = n \log X$.

Therefore a graph of $\log Y$ against $\log X$ gives a straight line with gradient equal to n and a $\log Y$ intercept equal to $\log k$. By measuring the gradient, assuming a straight line results from the log–log plot, then the power of X can be determined. If the log–log plot does not give a straight line, then the link is not of the form $Y = kX^n$.

Some common graph shapes

Parabolic curves describe the flight paths of projectiles or any other objects acted on by a constant force. The path of an electron beam between oppositely charged parallel plates is parabolic; each electron is acted on by a constant force.

The general equation for a parabola is $y = kx^2$. Figure 4.10 shows the shape of the parabola $y = 3x^2$. Equations of the form $x = ky^2$ are parabolic, but they are symmetrical about the x-axis not the y-axis. Figure 4.11 shows the curve for $x = y^2$.

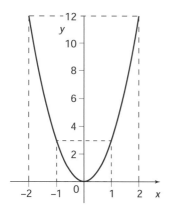

Fig 4.10 $y = 3x^2$

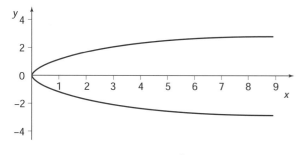

Fig 4.11 $x = y^2$

Compare the equations for projectiles and electron beams given in the table at the top of the next column. In both cases, suppose the initial velocity is u at right angles to the field lines.

Both equations are in the form $y = kx^2$, although k differs in each case. Figure 4.12 shows the shape of the trajectories.

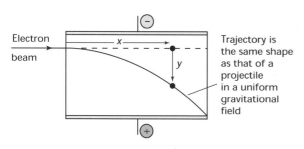

Fig 4.12 Parabolic paths

Force	Projectile mg (g = gravitational field strength)	Electron beam eE (E = electric field strength)
Acceleration	g	$\dfrac{eE}{m}$
Time to travel distance x across field (T)	x/u	x/u
Displacement at right angles to field (y)	$\dfrac{1}{2}\left(\dfrac{g}{u^2}\right)x^2$	$\dfrac{1}{2}\left(\dfrac{eE}{mu^2}\right)x^2\left(=\dfrac{1}{2}at^2\right)$

Hyperbolic curves are curves like p against V for Boyle's law (see Fig 4.8). The general equation for a hyperbola is $y = k/x$, where k is a constant. As Fig 4.8 shows, the curve tends towards either axis but never actually meets the axes; the correct mathematical word for 'tending towards but never meeting' is **asymptotic**.

Inverse-square law curves occur in gravitation and electric field theory and radioactivity (intensity of γ-radiation). The general equation is $y = k/x^2$, where k is a constant. So if x is doubled, y changes by a factor of 1/4. The shape of the curve is shown in Fig 4.13. Such curves show asymptotic behaviour at both axes.

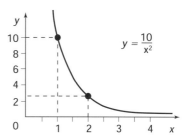

Fig 4.13 An inverse square curve

Exponential curves arise whenever the rate of change of any quantity is proportional to the quantity itself. Figure 4.14 shows an exponential

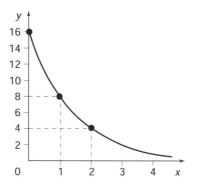

Fig 4.14 An exponential decrease

decrease curve. The key features of such curves are:

- At $x = 0$, the y-value is non-zero.
- The y-value drops by 50% in equal intervals of the x-variable.
- The curve is asymptotic at the x-axis; in other words, it never actually touches the x-axis.

In fact, the y-value drops by a constant factor for *any* equal set of intervals along the x-axis; let the y-value at $x = 0$ be y_0. Then, the interval from y_0 to $0.7y_0$ is the same as from $0.7y_0$ to $0.49y_0$ ($= 0.7 \times 0.7y_0$).

Labelling graphs

Scales along the axes of a graph are numerical. The axes must be labelled with the appropriate physical quantity named. The unit of the quantity and any prefix must be stated. Only if the axes are labelled can the physical quantities be read off the graph. The convention for labelling an axis is:

Name of physical quantity, symbol/prefix + unit.

Some examples are:

- pressure, p/kPa
- volume, V/m^3
- $1/\text{volume}, \dfrac{1}{V}/\text{m}^{-3}$

Powers of ten are included with the unit (and prefix, if any).

- pressure, $p/10^5 \text{ Pa}$
- capacitance, $C/10^{-6} \text{ F}$

Although in this last case it would be more common to use the prefix μ to represent 10^{-6} and so it would be written as:

- capacitance, $C/\mu\text{F}$

Reading off the graph scale gives a number equal to the quantity/unit. Suppose the graph is pressure against volume and a point on the graph has coordinates (110, 0.0012) with the axes labelled as in the first two examples above. Then the pressure/kPa = 110 hence pressure = 110 kPa. Also, volume/m^3 = 0.0012, so volume = 0.0012 m^3.

 ## Rates of change

Gradients and graphs

For a straight line the gradient is constant. Any section of a straight line can be used to form a right-angled triangle as in Fig 4.15. The gradient is defined as the change of the y-value/the change of the x-value. To measure the gradient of a straight line, the triangle should be as large as possible, to increase accuracy. Examples of constant gradients in physics include:

- the fall of temperature along a uniform heat-conducting lagged bar.
- the change of potential between two oppositely

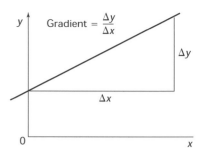

Fig 4.15 Constant gradient

charged parallel plates along a line at right angles to the plates from one to the other.

For a curve the gradient changes along the curve. The gradient at any point on the curve is equal to the gradient of the tangent at that point. To see why, mark any two points on a curve and join them by a straight line. Now repeat with one of the points moved closer to the other; the straight line is now closer in direction to the curve. If the two points are very close, the straight line between them is almost along the curve; the gradient of the line is then virtually the same as the gradient of the curve at that position. (See Fig 4.16.)

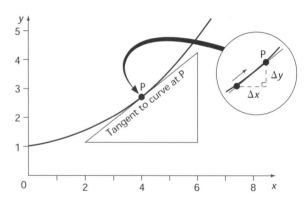

Fig 4.16 Tangents and curves

If the difference between the x-coordinates is Δx, and the difference in the y-coordinates is Δy for the two points, then the gradient of the line is $\Delta y/\Delta x$. As the two points are moved closer and closer, $\Delta x \to 0$ and $\Delta y/\Delta x$ becomes equal to the gradient of the curve there. The curve gradient is written $\dfrac{dy}{dx}$ where $\dfrac{d}{dx}$ means 'rate of change'. So the gradient of the curve $\dfrac{dy}{dx}$ equals $\dfrac{\Delta y}{\Delta x}$ as $\Delta x \to 0$.

To measure the gradient of a curve, use a plane mirror as in Fig 4.17. The mirror is placed at right angles to the curve where the curve and its image are smoothly continuous at the mirror; then the normal to the curve is drawn. The mirror can be used to draw a line at right angles to the normal, the new line touching the curve to give the gradient of the tangent at that point.

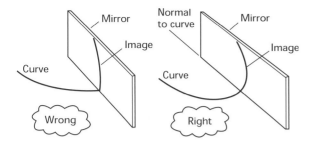

Fig 4.17 Measuring the gradient of a curve

Differentiation can be used to determine the gradient of a 'known' curve. For example, consider the curve $y = x^2$ shown in Fig 4.18.

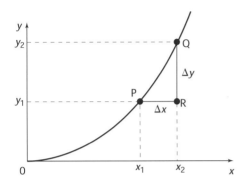

Fig 4.18 Differentiation

At point P, the coordinates are (x_1, y_1) where $y_1 = x_1^2$.
At point Q, the coordinates are (x_2, y_2) where $y_2 = x_2^2$.
The triangle PQR has height $\Delta y = y_2 - y_1$, and base $\Delta x = x_2 - x_1$.
The gradient of the triangle $= \Delta y / \Delta x$.
Now $\Delta y = y_2 - y_1 = x_2^2 - x_1^2 = (x_1 + \Delta x)^2 - x_1^2$
so $\Delta y = 2x_1 \Delta x + \Delta x^2$

Hence the gradient of the curve at x_1, $\left(\dfrac{dy}{dx}\right)_{x_1}$ is given by

$$\left(\frac{dy}{dx}\right)_{x_1} = \left(\frac{\Delta y}{\Delta x}\right)_{\Delta x \to 0} = 2x_1$$

So $\dfrac{dy}{dx} = 2x$ for $y = x^2$.

The general rule for differentiation of the function $y = ax^n$ can be worked out in a similar way. The result is $\dfrac{dy}{dx} = nax^{n-1}$. Likewise, the rules of trigonometry can be used for the differentiation of sines and cosines.

y	$\dfrac{dy}{dx}$
ax^n	nax^{n-1}
$\sin x$	$\cos x$
$\cos x$	$-\sin x$

Figure 4.4 shows that the gradient of the sine curve follows a cosine curve and it shows that the gradient of the cosine curve follows a (–sine) curve.

Turning points on curves are where the gradient is zero. On one side of a turning point, the gradient is positive and on the other side it is negative. For example, consider an object projected directly upwards at initial speed u. Figure 4.19(a) shows how the vertical height gain y changes with time; at maximum height, the gradient of the curve is zero so the vertical component of velocity is momentarily zero at this point. The gradient at any point is equal to the rate of change of vertical displacement i.e. the vertical component of velocity. Figure 4.19(b) shows how the gradient varies with time; the gradient of *this* curve is constant, equal to the acceleration due to gravity.

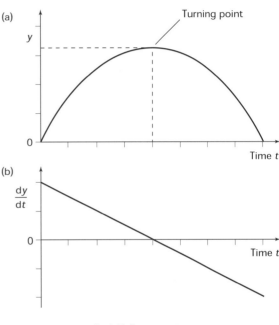

Fig 4.19 Turning points

Areas and integration

Areas under curves or under lines can give useful information if the product of the y-variable and the x-variable represent another physical variable. For example, consider Fig 4.6 which is a graph of tension against extension for a spring. Since tension × extension is 'force × distance' which equals work done, then the area under the line represents work done. Figure 4.20 shows a typical tension against extension curve for a rubber band; unlike Fig 4.6, the area under the curve is not a triangle so it is not so easy to determine, but it still represents work done. Each 'block' of area corresponds to a force of 0.1 N moved by a distance of 0.01 m. So each block represents 0.001 J of work (= 0.1 N × 0.01 m). The total work done to extend the rubber band by 0.07 m is therefore 0.022 J since the area under the curve (shown shaded) up to 0.07m is about 22 blocks.

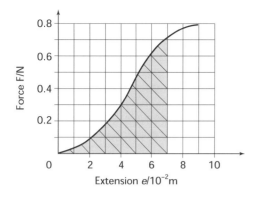

Fig 4.20 Using areas

The product of the *y*-variable and the *x*-variable *must* represent a physical variable if the area is to have any meaning or use. A graph of mass against volume for different sizes of the same material gives a straight line through the origin. The mass is proportional to the volume, and the gradient of the line gives the density. But the area under the line has no physical meaning since mass × volume does not represent a physical variable.

Other examples of curves where area is useful include:

- force against time where the area between the curve and the time-axis represents change of momentum.
- power against time where the area between the curve and the time-axis represents energy.
- potential difference against charge, where the area between the curve and the charge-axis represents energy.

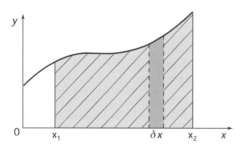

Fig 4.21 Integration

Let's see why the area in each case represents a physical variable. And why is the area usually between the curve and the *x*-axis? A small increase of the *x*-variable, δx (δ for small) gives little or no change of the *y*-variable. So the area under that section of the curve is a strip of width δx and height *y* which equals $y\delta x$. Hence the total area from x_1 to x_2, as in Fig 4.21, is equal to the area of all the small strips, each of width δx, from x_1 to x_2. Adding the individual strip areas together to give the total area is called **integrating** the curve.

For example, Fig 4.22 shows a curve of power *P* against time *t*. The work done in a short interval δt

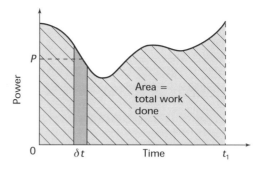

Fig 4.22 Power curves

is $P\delta t$, where *P* is the power at that point. So we write

$$\delta W = \delta dt$$

for the small amount of work done.

The total work done from $t = 0$ to $t = t_1$ is represented by the total area under the curve from 0 to t_1.

$$\text{Work done } W = \int_{t=0}^{t=t_1} P\,\mathrm{d}t$$

where ∫ is the integration sign.

Integration is the reverse process of differentiation. As Fig 4.22 shows, the work done in a short interval Δt is given by $\Delta W = P\Delta t$. Hence, *P* is $\Delta W/\Delta t$. So for

$$\Delta t \to 0,\ P = \frac{\mathrm{d}W}{\mathrm{d}t}.$$

The *y*-variable must be equal to the rate of change of area with *x*. In general terms,

$$\text{Area } A = \int y\,\mathrm{d}x$$

$$\text{and } y = \frac{\mathrm{d}A}{\mathrm{d}x}$$

Force-field curves representing the inverse square law of force give areas representing potential energy. Consider two point charges q_1 and q_2 at distance apart *r*. The force between the charges is given by

$$\text{Force } F = \frac{q_1 q_2}{4\pi\varepsilon_0} \times \frac{1}{r^2}$$

The work done by this force when the charges move apart from *r* to $r + \Delta r$ is $F\Delta r$. This amount of work is done by the charges so their P.E. (E_p) is lowered. Hence the change of P.E., $\Delta E_p = -F\Delta r$. So we can write

$$F = -\frac{\mathrm{d}E_p}{\mathrm{d}r}$$

Therefore, since the force is given by the inverse square law,

$$\frac{\mathrm{d}E_p}{\mathrm{d}r} = -\frac{q_1 q_2}{4\pi\varepsilon_0} \times \frac{1}{r^2} = \frac{k}{r^2}$$

where k is the constant $\dfrac{-q_1 q_2}{4\pi\varepsilon_0}$.

Because integration is the reverse of differentiation, the formula for E_p can be worked out accordingly. The result is

$$E_p = -\frac{k}{r}$$

Check that the differentiating $-k/r$ gives k/r^2.

Hence $E_p = \dfrac{q_1 q_2}{4\pi\varepsilon_0} \times \dfrac{1}{r}$

The inverse square law of force also applies to gravitation; the constant k is written as $-GMm$ for gravitational formulae.

Exponential processes

Exponential changes occur when the rate of change of a quantity is proportional to the quantity. Consider a physical quantity Q that changes with time. Its rate of change is $\dfrac{dQ}{dt}$, so an exponential process is where $\dfrac{dQ}{dt}$ is proportional to Q.

$$\frac{dQ}{dt} = kQ$$

where k is the constant of proportionality.
Suppose $k = 1$; the solution of the equation is the function

$$Q = Q_0\left(1 + t + \frac{t^2}{2!} + \frac{t^3}{3!} + \dots\right)$$

where Q_0 is a constant and $n!$ means $n(n-1)(n-2)\dots 3 \times 2 \times 1$. The $!$ symbol is called 'factorial' so 3 factorial $= 3! = 3 \times 2 \times 1 = 6$. This complicated-looking function is called the *exponential function*; its special feature is evident when it is differentiated term by term.

$$\frac{dQ}{dt} = Q_0\left(0 + 1 + t + \frac{t^2}{2!} + \dots\right)$$

So $\dfrac{dQ}{dt} = Q$

The exponential function shown above is written in short form as

$$Q = Q_0 e^t \quad \text{where } e^t = 1 + t + t^2/2! + t^3/3! + \dots$$

Suppose $Q_0 = 1$; after a short interval Δt, $Q + \Delta Q = e^{t + \Delta t}$ where ΔQ is the change of Q in that time interval.

Hence $\Delta Q = e^{t + \Delta t} - Q = Qe^{\Delta t} - Q$

So $\Delta Q = Q(e^{\Delta t} - 1)$

$$= Q\left(1 + \Delta t + \frac{\Delta t^2}{2!} + \dots - 1\right)$$

$$= Q\left(\Delta t + \frac{\Delta t^2}{2!} + \frac{\Delta t^3}{3!} + \dots\right)$$

Therefore $\dfrac{\Delta Q}{\Delta t} = Q\left(1 + \dfrac{\Delta t}{2!} + \dfrac{\Delta t^2}{3!} + \dots\right)$

Now $\dfrac{dQ}{dt} = \left(\dfrac{\Delta Q}{\Delta t}\right)_{\Delta t \to 0}$

So $\dfrac{dQ}{dt} = Q$

since all the terms but the first one in the bracket for $\dfrac{\Delta Q}{\Delta t}$ become zero as $\Delta t \to 0$.

So the equation $\dfrac{dQ}{dt} = Q$ has the solution $Q = Q_0 e^t$ where e^t is the exponential function equal to $1 + t + t^2/2! + t^3/3! + \dots$ The exponential number, e, is equal to 2.718 which is the value of the above function when $t = 1$.

For the equation $\dfrac{dQ}{dt} = kQ$

the solution is $Q = Q_0 e^{kt}$.

Note: The above equation may be written

$$\int_{Q_0}^{Q} \frac{dQ}{Q} = \int_{0}^{t} k\,dt$$

This has been a solution of the form
$$\ln Q - \ln Q_0 = kt$$
which gives $\quad Q = Q_0 e^{kt}$

All exponential processes involve functions of the form e^{kt} since these functions describe situations where the rate of change is proportional to the quantity.

Natural logarithms written ln or $\log_e$, are based on the exponential number e. The natural log of a number is the power that e must be raised to in order to equal the number.

From $Q = e^t$, then $t = \ln Q$ by definition of the natural log.

Exponential decrease

This is where a quantity **decreases** at a rate that is proportional to the quantity.

$$\frac{dQ}{dt} = -\lambda Q$$

where λ is called the **decay constant**.
The $-$ sign in the equation indicates that the rate of change is negative, so Q is a decreasing quantity.

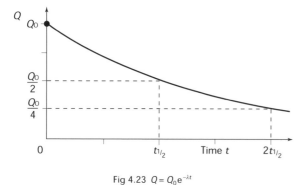

Fig 4.23 $Q = Q_0 e^{-\lambda t}$

The general solution of the equation is written

$$Q = Q_0 e^{-\lambda t}$$

where Q_0 is the initial value.

The graph of $Q = Q_0 e^{-\lambda t}$ is shown in Fig 4.23. As t becomes greater, the value of $e^{-\lambda t}$ becomes smaller so the curve tends towards the t-axis asymptotically. Another key feature of the curve is that Q drops by a constant factor in equal intervals of time.

The time constant for the process is the time taken for Q to fall to $1/e$ of its initial value.

$Q = Q_0 e^{-1}$ when $\lambda t = 1$.

Hence the time constant = $1/\lambda$.

Time constants occur in the theory of capacitor discharge circuits. The decay constant is $1/RC$ so the time constant is RC. (R = resistance, C = capacitance.)

The half-life $t_{1/2}$ for the process is the time for Q to fall to half its initial value.

Hence $0.5Q_0 = Q_0 e^{-\lambda t}$
Therefore $e^{\lambda t} = 2$

$$\lambda t = \ln 2$$

The bigger the decay constant, the shorter the half-life, so the faster the rate of decay.

A numerical approach to exponential decay is helpful for understanding the equations better. Rewrite the equation $\dfrac{dQ}{dt} = -\lambda Q$ as

$$\Delta Q = -\lambda Q \Delta t$$

Let $\lambda = 0.1$ and $Q_0 = 100$. Consider intervals $\Delta t = 1$. So $\Delta Q = -0.1Q$ gives the fall of Q over each interval. Now consider the sequence from $t = 0$.

t	0	1	2	3	4	5	6	7	8
Q	100	90	81	72.9	65.6	59.0	53.1	47.8	43.0
ΔQ	−10	−9	−8.1	−7.3	−6.6	−5.9	−5.3	−4.8	−4.3

Figure 4.24 shows how Q changes step-by-step with time. The half-life of the 'step' curve is 6.5.

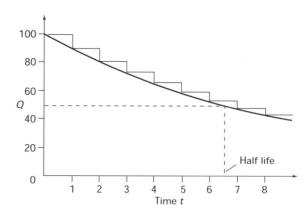

Fig 4.24 Step-by-step approach

The theoretical value, $(\ln 2)/\lambda$ is 6.9. The step-by-step approach becomes more accurate the smaller Δt is made.

Exponential increase

This is where the rate of **increase** of a quantity is proportional to the quantity.

$$\frac{dQ}{dt} = \alpha Q$$

where the constant $\alpha > 0$.

In this situation Q increases by a constant factor in equal intervals of time. Suppose $Q_0 = 100$, $\alpha = 0.1$ and $\Delta t = 1$. Then Q changes as below.

t	0	1	2	3	4	etc.
Q	100	110	121	133.1	146.4	
ΔQ	10	11	12.1	13.3	etc.	

Exponential increases are 'runaway' processes. Figure 4.25 shows how Q increases with t for the numerical example given.

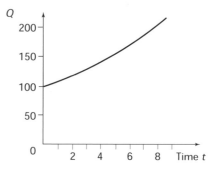

Fig 4.25 Exponential increase

Build-up exponentials

These occur where the rate of change **decreases from an initial non-zero value**. This type of situation is described by the equation

$$\frac{dQ}{dt} = A - \lambda Q$$

where A is a positive constant.

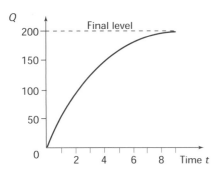

Fig 4.26 A build-up exponential

The rate of change, $\dfrac{dQ}{dt}$ is initially positive if we assume the initial value of Q is zero. So Q increases from zero, but increased Q makes $\dfrac{dQ}{dt}$ fall. So Q rises less and less rapidly, to reach a constant level as $t \to \infty$ when $\dfrac{dQ}{dt}$ becomes zero. The situation is shown by Fig 4.26 where the curve 'builds up' to a final level.

Physics situations where these type of curves occur include the following.

Terminal velocity reached when an object falls through a fluid. The drag force on the object due to the fluid is proportional to the object's speed v. So the resultant force F on the object is given by

$$F = \text{weight} - \text{drag force} = mg - kv$$

Also, acceleration $\dfrac{dv}{dt} = \dfrac{\text{force}}{\text{mass}} = g - \dfrac{kv}{m}$

where k is constant.

So Fig 4.26 also shows how the speed of such an object released from rest increases with time. Eventually, $\dfrac{dv}{dt}$ becomes zero so the terminal speed is given by mg/k.

Growth of direct current in a circuit with an inductor and a resistor in series. Figure 4.27 shows a simple circuit where the current builds up to a limit after the switch is closed. At any time after the switch is closed, the battery e.m.f. E is dropped across the resistor R and the inductor L. Hence,

$$E = \text{p.d. across } R + \text{p.d. across } L$$

So $E = IR + \dfrac{LdI}{dt}$

Therefore $\dfrac{dI}{dt} = \dfrac{E}{L} - \dfrac{R}{L}I$

The final value of current is when $\dfrac{dI}{dt}$ is zero, which means that E/R is the final current.

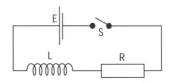

Fig 4.27 Current growth

Summary

Powers of ten
✓ $10^a \times 10^b = 10^{a+b}$
✓ $10^a/10^b = 10^{a-b}$
✓ If $x = 10^a$, then $a = \log_{10} x$

Trigonometry
✓ $\sin \theta = $ opposite/hypotenuse
✓ $\cos \theta = $ adjacent/hypotenuse
✓ $\tan \theta = $ opposite/adjacent
✓ $\sin^2 \theta + \cos^2 \theta = 1$
✓ arc length $s = r\theta$ for circle segment
✓ small angle approximation:
   $\sin \theta \approx \theta$ for angles less than about 10°

Graphs
✓ Equation for a straight line
   $y = mx + c$
   where m is the gradient and c is the y-intercept.

✓ For $y = kx^n$, $\log y = n \log x + \log k$
   so a graph of $\log y$ against $\log x$ gives a straight line.

Exponential decrease
✓ General equation $\dfrac{dQ}{dt} = -\lambda Q$
   where λ is the decay constant
✓ Solution $Q = Q_0 e^{-\lambda t}$
   $\ln Q = \ln Q_0 - \lambda t$

Short questions (see p.69 for answers)

1. Calculate
   a) $(3.2 \times 10^4)^2 \times 2 \times 10^{-4}$
   b) $(4.12 \times 10^{-3})^2 \times 1.4 \times 10^3$
   c) $\dfrac{(2.8 \times 10^5)^3}{1.5 \times 10^{-3}}$
   d) $\dfrac{1.4 \times 10^6}{(3.1 \times 10^5)^2}$
   e) $\dfrac{6.4 \times 10^8}{(4.1 \times 10^{-7})^2}$
   f) $(4.8 \times 10^2)^{1/2}$
   g) $(5.6 \times 10^8)^{3/2}$
   h) $(9.7 \times 10^5)^{-1/3}$
   i) $\dfrac{(6.3 \times 10^8)}{(2.4 \times 10^{-5})^{1/2}}$
   j) $(7.6 \times 10^4)^{-1/2}$

2. Use log tables to make each of the following calculations and check your answers using a calculator.
   a) 3.62×1.58
   b) 4.91×21.4
   c) $38.4/5.6$
   d) $61.4/0.159$
   e) $3.16 \times 22.1/0.86$
   f) $0.156/0.35$
   g) $31.6 \times 10^5/0.65$
   h) $2.15^{1/5}$
   i) $36.9^{1.4}$
   j) $(58.6/0.91)^{1/2}$

3. a) Measure the diameter of a 1p piece to the nearest mm. Calculate the angle subtended at your eye by a 1p piece held at a distance of 1m from your eye.
   b) Estimate the angular width of the Moon by holding a 1p piece at the distance from your eye at which it blocks out the lunar disc.

4. a) Plot the equations $y = x + 5$ and $2y = 7 - x$ over the range from $x = -10$ to $+10$. Write down the coordinates of the point (P) at which the two lines intercept.
   b) Write down the equation for the line OP, where O is the origin of the graph.

5. a) What is the equation of the straight line that passes through the two points $(x = 5, y = 0)$ and $(x = -2, y = 7)$? What is the value of the y-intercept of the line?
   b) Plot the line in a) and determine the least distance from the line to the origin.

6. Solve each of the following pairs of simultaneous equations.
   a) $3x + y = 6$; $y = 2x + 1$
   b) $3a - 2b = 8$; $a + b = 2$
   c) $5p + 2q = 18$; $q = 2p$
   d) $7 - y = 2x$; $x/3 = y$
   e) $u = 5/v$; $u + v = 6$

7. Each of the following relationships is between two variable quantities. Given the variable to be plotted along one particular axis, what function of the other variable would you plot along the other axis to give a straight line?

Variables	Relationship	Horizontal axis	Vertical axis
a) f and T	$f = \frac{1}{2}L \times \left(\dfrac{T}{\mu}\right)^{1/2}$	T	?
b) I and z	$I = I_0 e^{-\mu z}$	z	?
c) E and r	$E = k/r^2$	?	E
d) p and V	$P(V - b) = RT$	?	pV
e) C and t	$C - C_0 = Ae^{-\lambda t}$	t	?

8. Which graph A to E fits each of the equations below?
   a) $xy = $ constant
   b) $x + y = $ constant
   c) $y = Ae^{-kx}$ where A and k are constants
   d) $y = ($ constant $) x^2$
   e) $y - a = bx$ where a and b are constants.

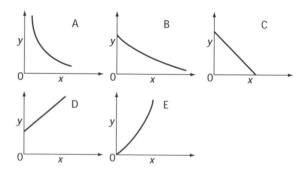

9. Differentiate each of the following functions with respect to x.
   a) $y = 3x^2$
   b) $y = 2x - x^2$
   c) $y = 3/x^2$
   d) $y = Ae^{-3x}$
   e) $y = \sin 2x$.

10. What physical variable is represented by the area under the curve of each of the following graphs?
    a) induced e.m.f. against time
    b) current against time
    c) pressure against volume
    d) stress against strain
    e) acceleration against time

11. For the equation $C = Ae^{-\mu x}$, when $x = 0$, $C = 100$. Also, when $x = 5$, $C = 36$. Calculate:
    a) the values of A and μ.
    b) the value of C for i) $x = 1$, ii) $x = 10$,
    c) the value of x when i) $C = 50$, ii) $C = 10$.

12. a) Plot a graph of the function $N = 1000\, e^{-5t}$ from $t = 0$ to $t = 1$. What is the 'half-life' of the curve?
    b) What is the ratio of the initial gradient to the gradient at one half-life?

Units

Base units

Units for measurement have always played an important part in the life of any community. In the Middle Ages, the unit of length was the yard, based at first on the circumference of a person's body, then later the length of Henry I's arm! Small wonder that units of those times varied from country to country, sometimes even within the same country. Clearly, a nationally agreed 'yard-stick' was an important development. Fortunately for us, scientists use an internationally agreed system of units called SI (*Système Internationale*) units. Communications between scientists in different countries or in different disciplines is much easier because of the use of a common system of units throughout the World.

The (SI) system is founded on seven **base units**, all of which are defined by international agreement. All other scientific units are derived from these seven base units.

The second (s) is the unit of time, defined in terms of the frequency of light from the caesium-133 atom.

The metre (m) is the unit of length, defined in terms of the distance travelled by light in a certain time.

The kilogram (kg) is the unit of mass, defined by an international prototype at Sevres, France.

The ampere (A) is the unit of current, defined in terms of the force between two parallel conductors (carrying equal current) 1 m apart.

The kelvin (K) is the unit of thermodynamic temperature.

The mole (mol) is the unit of amount of a substance.

The candela (cd) is the unit of luminous intensity. This unit does not feature in A-level courses.

The exact definitions of these base units are given in most physics reference books. Apart from the ampere, knowledge of the exact definitions is not required at A-level. Special laboratories in many countries use these definitions to calibrate instruments accurately for use by scientists outside these 'standards' laboratories. For example, the manufacturer of the 'humble' metre rule has a standard metre rule that is used to check the metre rules he makes; the standard metre rule would have been made in a 'standards' laboratory.

Each unit has a recognized symbol. The symbol is a small letter (or letters) unless it is the symbol of a unit named after a scientist (e.g. the ampere: A) where it is given a capital letter.

Prefixes used with SI units are as follows.

Prefix	atto	femto	pico	nano	micro	milli
Factor	10^{-18}	10^{-15}	10^{-12}	10^{-9}	10^{-6}	10^{-3}
Symbol	a	f	p	n	μ	m
Prefix	—	kilo	mega	giga	tera	
Factor	1	10^3	10^6	10^9	10^{12}	
Symbol	—	k	M	G	T	

For example, $6\mu A$ = 6 microamperes = 6×10^{-6}A.
Note: MΩ is pronounced megohm.

Derived units

All SI units that are not base units are defined in terms of base units. The derived units, as they are called, are built up 'step-by-step' from the base units using the known links between physical quantities. For example, the unit of speed is m s^{-1}; the negative index (e.g. '–1') is used for 'per'. So m s^{-1} means 'metres per second'. Figure 5.1 shows how some of the more common derived units are linked to the four base units, the metre, the kilogram, the second and the ampere.

Consider the following examples to see how they are linked to the base units.

The pascal (Pa) is the unit of pressure.
Pressure = force/area so 1 Pa = 1 N m^{-2}
Force = mass × acceleration so 1 N = 1 kg m s^{-2}
Hence 1 Pa = 1 kg m s^{-2} m^{-2} = 1 kg m^{-1} s^{-2}

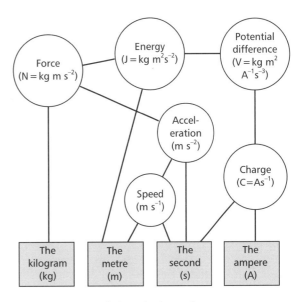

Fig 5.1 Using base units

Quantity	Symbol	Unit	Abbreviation	Base units
Speed or velocity	v	metre per second	m s^{-1}	m s^{-1}
Acceleration	a	metre per second per second	m s^{-2}	m s^{-2}
Force	F	newton	N	kg m s^{-2}
Energy or work	E or W	joule	J	kg m^2 s^{-2}
Power	P	watt	W	kg m^2 s^{-3}
Pressure	p	pascal	Pa	kg m^{-1} s^{-2}
Electric charge	Q	coulomb	C	A s
Potential difference	V	volt	V	kg m^2 s^{-3} A^{-1}
Resistance	R	ohm	Ω	kg m^2 s^{-3} A^{-2}
Capacitance	C	farad	F	A^2 s^4 kg^{-1} m^{-2}
Magnetic field strength	B	tesla	T	kg s^{-2} A^{-1}
Electric field strength	E	volt per metre	V m^{-1}	kg m s^{-3} A^{-1}
Magnetic flux	Φ	weber	Wb	kg m^2 s^{-2} A^{-1}
Temperature gradient	—	kelvin per metre	K m^{-1}	K m^{-1}

The volt (V) is the unit of potential difference.
Potential difference = work done/charge so
$1\ \text{V} = 1\ \text{J C}^{-1}$
Work = force × distance so
$1\ \text{J} = 1\ \text{N m} = 1\ \text{kg m}^2\ \text{s}^{-2}$ since $1\ \text{N} = 1\ \text{kg m s}^{-2}$
Charge = current × time so $1\ \text{C} = 1\ \text{A s}$
Hence $1\ \text{V} = 1\ \text{kg m}^2\ \text{s}^{-2}\ \text{A}^{-1}\ \text{s}^{-1} = 1\ \text{kg m}^2\ \text{s}^{-3}\ \text{A}^{-1}$

Now you can appreciate why we have *named* units. Imagine asking in your local shop for a 1.5 kg m^2 s^{-3} A^{-1} cell!

A list of the more common derived units is given in the table above. The abbreviation for each unit and the symbol for each quantity is also given. Take care not to confuse symbols for quantities (e.g. F for force) with the abbreviation for units (e.g. F for farad).

Symbols and formulae

It is the normal convention that the symbol for a physical quantity represents the magnitude *and* the unit of the quantity. For example, if the speed of an object is 3 m s^{-1}, then we write $v = 3$ m s^{-1}. Under the accepted convention, it is meaningless to write $v = 3$. Since each symbol represents magnitude and unit, then phrases such as 'Let the speed $= v$ m s^{-1}' are not correct; the statement would be the same as writing '$v = 3$ m s^{-1} m s^{-1}' if v was 3 m s^{-1}. Symbols must be used carefully in formulae and calculations.

For graphs the unit and any prefix of a physical quantity is written near the appropriate axis in the form 'symbol/(prefix + unit)'. For example, if you wish to show that the vertical-axis of a graph represents speed in mm s^{-1}, then the correct format to label the axis is

   speed v/mm s^{-1}.

Reading off the graph axis gives a number equal to v/mm s^{-1}. So, for example, if the reading gives v/mm s$^{-1} = 5$, then $v = 5$ mm s^{-1}. The prefix is sometimes replaced by powers of ten. So the label 'v/mm s^{-1}' could be written 'v/10^{-3} m s^{-1}'.

For calculations involving formulae, a helpful procedure is as follows.

STEP 1 List the value and unit of each 'known' quantity.

STEP 2 Convert all magnitudes to standard form, and all prefixes to powers of ten.

STEP 3 State the formula to be used.

STEP 4 Use the formula for the calculation.

STEP 5 Use the formula to work out the unit of the quantity to be calculated if its unit is not known.

For example, suppose you were given the heat radiation formula $P = \sigma AT^4$ for the power P radiated away from a hot wire of surface area A at surface temperature T, with the following instructions.

a) Show that the unit of σ, W m^{-2} K^{-4}, is equivalent to kg s^{-3} K^{-4}.

b) Calculate the surface temperature of a wire of length 326 mm and diameter 0.15 mm when the wire radiates power at 20 W, given $\sigma = 5.7 \times 10^{-8}$ W m^{-2} K^{-4}.

The equation can be rearranged to give $\sigma = P/AT^4$. So the base units of σ are the base units of P divided by the base units of AT^4. Hence 1 W m^{-2} K^{-4} is equal to 1 kg s^{-3} K^{-4}.

To calculate the surface temperature

$\sigma = 5.7 \times 10^{-8}$ W m^{-2} K^{-4}
$P = 20$ W
$A = $ surface area $= \pi \times$ diameter $\times$ length
$\quad = \pi \times 0.15 \times 10^{-3} \times 0.326$ m^2

Hence

$$T^4 = \frac{P}{\sigma A}$$

$$= \frac{20}{5.7 \times 10^{-8} \times \pi \times 0.326 \times 0.15 \times 10^{-3}}$$

So $T^4 = 2.29 \times 10^{12}$

Hence $T = 1230$ K

In the above example, the unit of the quantity to be calculated is known. Some formulae do not give such obvious units. Consider the equation for the drag force F on a sphere of radius r moving at speed v through a fluid of viscosity η.

$$F = 6\pi\eta r v$$

What are the base units of η? Rearrange the equation to make η its subject. So $\eta = F/(6\pi r v)$.

The unit of η is given by

$$\frac{\text{The unit of force}}{\text{Unit of } r} \times \text{unit of } v = \frac{\text{kg m s}^{-2}}{\text{m}} \times \text{m s}^{-1}$$
$$= \text{kg m}^{-1} \text{ s}^{-1}$$

 ## Dimensional analysis

The method of expressing any derived unit in terms of the base units can be taken one stage further to make it more formal. Each of the base quantities is called a 'dimension', and is given a special symbol.

Dimension	Dimension symbol
Mass	M
Length	L
Time	T
Current	A
Temperature	θ

Every other quantity can be expressed in these basic dimensions without reference to the actual base units. The dimensions of a quantity are indicated by the use of square brackets. For example, [speed] means 'the dimensions of speed' which are written LT^{-1} since speed is distance per unit time. The dimensions of each of the quantities listed below can be worked out in the same way as its base units; the links between each quantity and the base units are used.

Speed	$[v] = \text{L T}^{-1}$
Acceleration	$[a] = \text{L T}^{-2}$
Force	$[F] = \text{M L T}^{-2}$
Energy	$[E] = \text{M L}^2 \text{ T}^{-2}$
Power	$[P] = \text{M L}^2 \text{ T}^{-3}$
Pressure	$[p] = \text{M L}^{-1} \text{ T}^{-2}$
Charge	$[Q] = \text{A T}$
P.D.	$[V] = \text{M L}^2 \text{ T}^{-3} \text{ A}^{-1}$
Resistance	$[R] = \text{M L}^2 \text{ T}^{-3} \text{ A}^{-2}$
Capacitance	$[C] = \text{A}^2 \text{ T}^4 \text{ M}^{-1} \text{ L}^{-2}$

Using dimensions

To determine the dimensions or units of an expression in a formula. For example, suppose you wish to determine the base units of thermal conductivity k. The equation for thermal conductivity is

$Q/t = kA(T_1 - T_2)/L$
where Q/t is the heat flow/second,
$\quad A$ is the area of cross-section,
$\quad (T_1 - T_2)/L$ is the temperature gradient.
Hence $[Q/t] = [k] \times [A] \times [(T_1 - T_2)/L]$
$\quad [Q/t] = [Q]/[t] = [\text{energy}]/[t]$
$\qquad = [\text{M L}^2 \text{ T}^{-2}]/\text{T} = \text{M L}^2 \text{ T}^{-3}$
$\quad [A] = \text{L}^2$
$\quad [(T_1 - T_2)/L] = \theta \text{L}^{-1}$
So $\text{M L}^2 \text{ T}^{-3} = [k] \times \text{L}^2 \times \theta \text{L}^{-1} = [k]\theta \text{L}$

Giving $[k] = \dfrac{\text{M L}^2 \text{ T}^{-3}}{\text{L}\theta} = \text{M L T}^{-3} \theta^{-1}$

The base units for k are therefore kg m s^{-3} K^{-1}.

To check equations Suppose you want to check the link between the variables in the equation for the time constant of an inductor and resistor in series (i.e. growth of current in a series LR circuit). Perhaps you can't remember whether the time constant is RL or R/L or L/R.

$$[\text{Resistance}] = \frac{[\text{p.d.}]}{[\text{current}]}$$
$$= \frac{\text{M L}^2 \text{ T}^{-3} \text{A}^{-1}}{\text{A}} = \text{M L}^2 \text{ T}^{-3} \text{ A}^{-2}$$

$[\text{Inductance}]$

$$= \frac{[\text{induced e.m.f.}]}{[\text{rate of change of current}]} = \frac{[\text{V}]}{[\text{I}]/[\text{t}]}$$
$$= \frac{\text{M L}^2 \text{ T}^{-3} \text{ A}^{-1}}{\text{A T}^{-1}} = \frac{\text{M L}^2 \text{ T}^{-3} \text{ A}^{-2}}{\text{T}^{-1}}$$

Hence $[\text{inductance}] = \dfrac{[\text{resistance}]}{T^{-1}}$

So $T^{-1} = \dfrac{[\text{resistance}]}{[\text{inductance}]}$

Therefore the time constant is L/R.

To establish links between quantities in a given situation. For example, suppose we are given that the drag force F on a sphere moving through a fluid at steady speed depends on:

- the fluid viscosity η,
- the speed v,
- the sphere's radius r.

Write the link as an equation $F = k\eta^a v^b r^c$ where k is a numerical constant and a, b and c are powers to be determined. Since k is a numerical constant, it has no dimensions.
$[F] = [\eta^a] [v^b] [r^c]$
but $[F] = \text{M L T}^{-2}$,
$[\eta] = \text{M L}^{-1} \text{ T}^{-1}$
$\quad = [\text{stress}]/[\text{velocity gradient}]$
$\quad = [\text{force}]/[\text{area} \times \text{velocity gradient}]$
$\quad = \text{M L T}^{-2}/(\text{L}^2 \text{ T}^{-1})$
$[v] = \text{L T}^{-1}$
$[r] = \text{L}$
Hence $\text{M L T}^{-2} = (\text{M L}^{-1} \text{ T}^{-1})^a \times (\text{L T}^{-1})^b \times (\text{L})^c$
so $\text{M L T}^{-2} = \text{M}^a \text{L}^{-a} \text{T}^{-a} \times \text{L}^b \text{T}^{-b} \times \text{L}^c$
i.e. $\text{M L T}^{-2} = \text{M}^a \text{L}^{-a+b+c} \text{ T}^{-a-b}$

Dimensions of M: Left hand side = 1
  Right hand side = a hence $a = 1$
Dimensions of L: Left hand side = 1
  Right hand side = $-a + b + c$
  Hence $-a + b + c = 1$
Dimensions of T: Left hand side = -2
  Right hand side = $-a - b$
  Hence $-a - b = -2$

Since $a = 1$, the last equation ($-a - b = -2$) gives $b = 1$.

So the second equation ($-a + b + c = 1$) gives $c = 1$.

So $a = 1$, $b = 1$, $c = 1$.

Hence $F = k\eta rv$

The method cannot be used to determine the value of the numerical constant k but it does establish the link between the variables.

Treatment of errors

Types of error

An error in a measurement makes the measured value differ from the correct value. Measurement gives a value that may or may not be the correct value because errors may be present. So how can the correct value be determined? The best that can be done is to state **the probable error** when a measurement is made. For example, if the diameter of a wire is measured at 0.36 mm with a probable error of 0.02 mm, then the correct value is in the range 0.34 to 0.38 mm. The diameter is written as 0.36 ± 0.02 mm where ± 0.02 mm is the probable error and 0.36 mm is the value of the measurement.

The percentage probable error or just the percentage error, is the probable error converted to a percentage of the measurement. So the percentage error in the diameter measurement above is 5.5%. Resistors and capacitors are usually coded so that the percentage error or **tolerance** can be seen by inspection; for example, a resistor with a gold tolerance band has a tolerance of 5%. If the resistor's value is 100 ohms, then its resistance is in the range from 95 ohms to 105 ohms.

Errors in measurements are caused in many ways. If the sensitivity of an instrument decreases after its initial calibration, then the instrument will consistently read 'low'; its reading will always be less than the correct value because the instrument has become less sensitive. This is an example of a **systematic error**. Such errors can be difficult to detect. Sometimes they only become obvious when the results are plotted on a graph. Recalibrating meters, checking zero errors, using a plane mirror to read a scale, as in Fig 5.2 are all ways of avoiding systematic errors.

Random errors are evident when repeated measurements of the same quantity in the same situation give different readings. Try timing an oscillating body for ten cycles; repeat your timing a few times to give several values of the time for ten

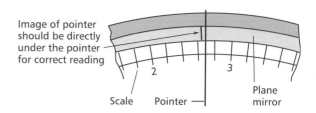

Fig 5.2 Using a plane mirror

cycles, and you ought to find there is a spread of values. The probable error gives the range which most of the readings lie in. The mean value of the readings is calculated by adding the readings together then dividing the sum by the total number of readings. By making as many timings as possible, the probable error is reduced and so the mean value is more accurate; in other words, the mean value is closer to the true value. Suppose the timings were: 20.2 s, 19.6 s, 20.0 s, 20.1 s, 19.8 s, 19.6 s, 19.9 s, 20.2 s, 20.0 s and 20.1 s.

The mean value = sum of all ten timings/10
  = 19.95 s.

The probable error = ± 0.2 s.

Hence the timing = 20.0 ± 0.2 s, since the value of 19.95 is rounded up to 20.0 so that it is stated with the same number of decimal places as the probable error. Otherwise, 19.95 implies precision to within ± 0.05 s which is not true.

If all the readings are the same, then the probable error is given by the precision with which the reading is made.

Plotting errors

When a variable quantity is measured at different intervals on a scale, the usual practice is to estimate the probable error from the precision with which the scale can be read. For example, Fig 5.2 shows the scale of 0–5 A ammeter; the scale can be read to a precision of 0.2 A, so the probable error of a single reading is ± 0.2 A. Random errors that occur when a set of readings is made off a scale can be dealt with by graphs.

A straight line graph can be plotted if the relationship between the variables is known. For example, consider the measurements made in a simple pendulum experiment to determine g (the acceleration due to gravity) given in the table on the next page.

The time period is given by the equation

$$T = 2\pi \sqrt{\frac{L}{g}}$$

Hence $T^2 = \dfrac{4\pi^2 L}{g}$

A graph of T^2 against L should give a straight line through the origin. The gradient of the line is equal to $4\pi^2/g$, so by measuring the gradient, the value of g can be calculated.

The probable errors in the measurements can be

Length of pendulum L/mm	200	400	600	800	1000 ± 4 mm
Time for 20 oscillations/s	18.2	25.4	31.4	35.5	40.0
	18.1	25.7	31.4	35.7	40.4
	17.8	25.3	30.9	35.8	40.4
Average time for 20 oscillations/s	18.0	25.5	31.2	35.7	40.3 ± 0.2 s
Time period T/s	0.90	1.28	1.56	1.79	2.02 ± 0.01 s

shown on the graph by using the 'box' method shown in Fig 5.3. Each box has width corresponding to the probable error of ±4 mm in the length measurement. The height of each box isn't so easy to deal with because the vertical axis represents T^2 not T. The most straightforward approach is to start with the range of each value.

For $L = 200$ mm, T is in the range 0.89 to 0.91 s.

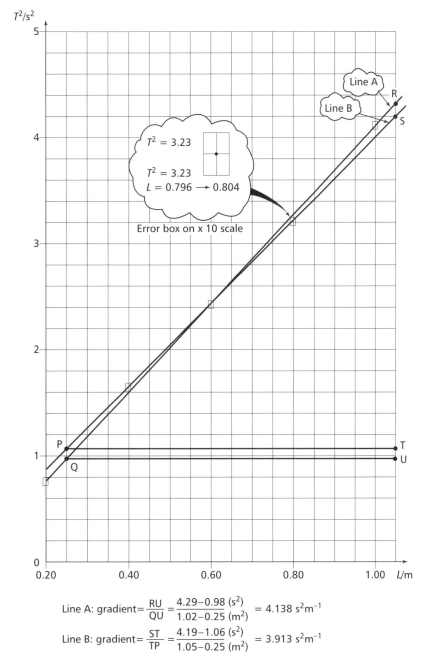

Line A: gradient $= \dfrac{RU}{QU} = \dfrac{4.29-0.98 \ (s^2)}{1.02-0.25 \ (m^2)} = 4.138 \ s^2m^{-1}$

Line B: gradient $= \dfrac{ST}{TP} = \dfrac{4.19-1.06 \ (s^2)}{1.05-0.25 \ (m^2)} = 3.913 \ s^2m^{-1}$

Fig 5.3 Showing errors on graphs

So T^2 is in the range from 0.79 to 0.83 s²; the value of T^2 is 0.81 ± 0.02 s². The height of the error box in this case is therefore 0.04 s². The other box heights can be calculated in the same way.

L/m	0.200	0.400	0.600	0.800	1.000 ± 4 mm
T^2/s^2	0.81	1.63	2.43	3.19	4.06
Probable error in T^2/s^2	±0.02	±0.03	±0.03	±0.04	±0.04

Figure 5.3 shows two straight lines drawn through the error boxes. Line A is as steep as possible, passing through each box. Line B is the line with the least possible gradient that passes through the boxes. The two lines therefore give the maximum and the minimum possible gradient, according to the errors. So an average value *and* a probable error can be determined for the gradient.

Line A gradient = 4.138 s² m⁻¹
Line B gradient = 3.913 s² m⁻¹.

Hence the average value of the gradient = 4.03 s² m⁻¹, and the probable error is ±0.11 s² m⁻¹.

$$\frac{4\pi^2}{g} = 4.03 \pm 0.11 \text{ s}^2 \text{ m}^{-1}$$

The maximum value of $\dfrac{4\pi^2}{g} = 4.14$, so the minimum value of g is $4\pi^2/4.14 = 9.54$ m s⁻².

The minimum value of $\dfrac{4\pi^2}{g} = 3.91$, so the maximum value of g is $4\pi^2/3.91 = 10.12$ m s⁻².
Hence $g = 9.83 \pm 0.29$ m s⁻².

Curve fitting is necessary if a straight line graph is not possible. The curve should be drawn so that it passes smoothly through all the error boxes. If the

gradient changes sharply, then more measurements need to be made to define the curve more closely in that area. For example, suppose you are investigating the current against voltage characteristic for a silicon diode; typical results are shown in Fig 5.4. The gradient changes sharply at about 0.5 V. So as many measurements as possible in this part need to be made.

Combining errors

Add the probable errors where the change of a quantity is to be calculated. For example, suppose a travelling microscope is used to measure the distance across ten fringe widths in an interference experiment. The cross-wires of the microscope are centred on one of the dark fringes, as in Fig 5.5. The reading of the microscope's vernier scale, x_1, is recorded. Then the cross-wires are moved along a line at right angles to the fringes across ten fringe spacings. The reading at this new position, x_2, is then recorded. The precision which each reading is made with is determined by the contrast of the fringes. So a probable error e for each reading is estimated.

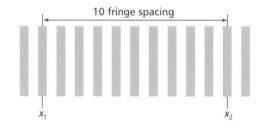

Fig 5.5 Adding errors

Suppose $x_1 = 3.5 \pm 0.1$ mm i.e. x_1 is from 3.4 to 3.6 mm.
$x_2 = 6.6 \pm 0.1$ mm i.e. x_2 is from 6.5 to 6.7 mm.

So the difference $x_2 - x_1$ is in the range from 2.9 (= 6.5 − 3.6) to 3.3 mm (=6.7 − 3.4).
Hence $x_1 - x_2 = 3.1 \pm 0.2$ mm.

The probable error in the difference of the two readings is obtained by adding the individual errors.

Percentage probable errors are added where quantities are to be multiplied or divided by one another. For example, suppose we wish to calculate the average speed of a ball bearing falling through a vertical tube of water.

Light gates could be used to time the ball as it falls through a measured distance. Several timings would need to be made, releasing the ball from rest at the same point each time. Suppose the readings are as follows.

Position of first light gate = 21 ± 2 mm
Position of second light gate = 224 ± 2 mm
Timings/ms 531 548 564 542 535
Hence distance fallen $D = 203 \pm 4$ mm

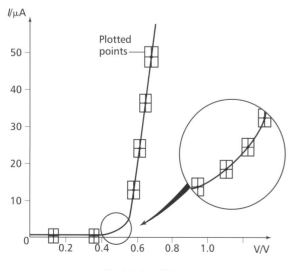

Fig 5.4 Curve fitting

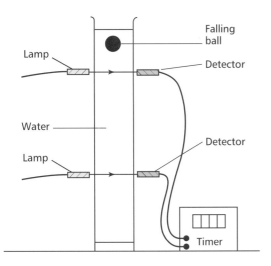

Fig 5.6 Adding percentage errors

$$= \frac{D}{T}(1 \pm \Delta D/D) \times (1 \mp \Delta T/T)$$

$$= \frac{D}{T}(1 \pm \Delta D/D \pm \Delta T/T)$$

again neglecting second order terms.

So if the average speed is $V \pm \Delta V$, which equals $V(1 \pm \Delta V/V)$, then $\Delta V/V = \Delta D/D + \Delta T/T$.

Hence the percentage error in V is the sum of the percentage errors in D and T.

When quantities are multiplied or divided, the percentage error in the final value is the product of the individual percentage errors. If a quantity in the formula is to the power n, then that quantity contributes n times its individual percentage error to the total error. For example, the formula for the flow rate of a viscous liquid through a pipe is

$$Q/t = \frac{pR^4}{8\eta L}$$

where Q/t = volume per second,
$\quad p$ = pressure across ends,
$\quad L$ = pipe length,
$\quad R$ = pipe radius,
$\quad \eta$ = fluid viscosity.

To calculate η from measurements of all the other quantities, the formula must be rearranged to give

$$\eta = \frac{pR^4}{8LQ/t}$$

The total percentage error = percentage error in p + percentage error in R^4 + percentage error in L + percentage error in Q/t.

However, the percentage error in R^4 is four times the percentage error in R. So the contribution from the percentage error in R is much more significant than the other contributions. If R, L, Q/t and p are each measured accurate to 2%, the total percentage error is 14%; R contributes 8% of the 14% total. To reduce the contribution from R^4 down to 2%, the error in R must be cut down to 0.5%. So R must be measured much more accurately than the other quantities.

and the average time $T = 544 \pm 15$ ms
The average speed = $D/T = 0.373$ mm ms^{-1}
$\qquad\qquad\qquad = 0.373$ m s^{-1}
The percentage error for the average speed
= percentage error for D + percentage error for T
Percentage error for $D = 4 \times 100/203 = 2\%$
Percentage error for $T = 15 \times 100/544 = 2.8\%$
So the percentage error for the speed = 4.8%
Therefore the probable error for the speed is $4.8 \times 0.373/100 = 0.018$ m s^{-1}.
Average speed = 0.373 ± 0.018 m s^{-1}.

To understand why the percentage errors are added, consider the example again.

$$\text{Average speed} = \frac{D \pm \Delta D}{T \pm \Delta T} = \frac{(D \pm \Delta D)}{(T \pm \Delta T)} \times \frac{(T \mp \Delta T)}{(T \mp \Delta T)}$$

However $(T \pm \Delta T)(T \mp \Delta T) = T^2$, neglecting the second order of the term ΔT^2 since it is very small compared with the others.
Hence the average speed

$$= (D \pm \Delta D) \times \frac{(T \mp \Delta T)}{T^2}$$

Summary

Units

✓ The most commonly-used base units are the metre (m); the kilogram (kg); the second (s); the ampere (A).

✓ Each derived unit can be written as a combination of base units.

✓ The base dimensions are mass M, length L, time T, current A and temperature. The dimensions of any physical quantity can be written in terms of the base dimensions.

Errors

✓ The probable error of a measurement gives the range which the correct value will nearly always lie in.

✓ The percentage error of a measurement is $100 \times$ the probable error/the measurement.

✓ Where quantities are added or subtracted from one another, the total probable error is the sum of the individual errors.

✓ Where quantities are multiplied or divided, the total percentage error is the product of the individual percentage errors.

 Short questions (see p. 69 for answers)

1. Express each of the following quantities in terms of the base units of the SI system.
   a) momentum
   b) resistivity
   c) thermal conductivity
   d) density
   e) electric field constant, ε_0.

2. Show that each of the following equations is dimensionally correct.
   a) Time constant = RC,
      where R = resistance,
      C = capacitance.
   b) Speed of light $c = \left(\dfrac{1}{\mu_0 \varepsilon_0}\right)^{1/2}$

      where μ_0 = magnetic field constant,
      ε_0 = electric field constant.
   c) Energy stored = $\frac{1}{2} CV^2$,
      where C = capacitance,
      V = p.d.

   d) Time period of a simple pendulum $T = 2\pi \sqrt{\dfrac{L}{g}}$

      where L = length.

   e) Speed of waves on a stretched wire $c = \left(\dfrac{T}{\mu}\right)^{1/2}$

      where T = tension
      μ = mass per unit length.

3. In an experiment to measure the density of a ball bearing, the following readings were obtained.
   mass = 7.06 ± 0.02g
   diameter = 12.06 ± 0.04 mm
   Calculate
   a) the percentage error of each measurement,
   b) the value of the density,
   c) the percentage error in the density value.

4. In an experiment to determine g, the acceleration of free fall, a steel ball bearing was timed falling from rest through a distance D. The readings obtained were as follows.
   $D = 1.215 \pm 0.004$ m.
   Time taken = 495, 498, 503, 496, 501ms.
   Calculate
   a) the percentage error in D and t, the time taken,
   b) the value of g,
   c) the percentage error in g.

5. Discuss the accuracy of the falling ball method for g compared with the simple pendulum method.

 Longer questions (see p. 69 for answers)

6. (45 min) This question is about drag, or resistance to motion acting on a high speed train. The drag is thought to be given by the equation
   $F = A + Bv + Cv^2$
   where F is the drag in kN, v is the velocity of the train in ms^{-1}, and A, B and C are constants. The table below gives the observations made in a test in which the drag was measured at various train velocities.

Velocity in m s^{-1}	Drag in kN
5	3.3
10	4.4
15	6.0
20	8.2
25	10.9
30	14.0
35	17.8
40	22.0
45	26.8

   a) Plot a graph of drag (y-axis) against velocity (x-axis).
   b) Use your graph to estimate the value of A.
   c) If the drag equation is correct, the slope S of the graph will be given by the equation
      $S = B + 2Cv$
      (i) Measure the slope of the graph for train velocities of 10 m s^{-1}, 20 m s^{-1}, 30 m s^{-1} and 40 m s^{-1} showing how you obtained your values. Tabulate your results.
      (ii) Plot a suitable graph to test the relationship and use your graph to determine values for B and C. In each case explain how you obtained the result.

   (AEB)

7. (Approx. 30 min.) A Geiger-Muller tube was fixed with its axis horizontal at a place on a bench well-removed from all known radioactive sources. Background count-rate measurements were made by recording counts over several ten-minute periods. The following counts were obtained for five such periods:
   290, 277, 273, 263 and 247.
   Find the mean background count-rate in counts per minute.

A weak radioactive source was then mounted on the axis of the tube with its protective grille facing the end-window of the tube, so that it could be moved along the axis to give various distances s between the grille and the end-window, as in the figure below.

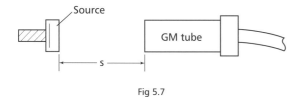

Fig 5.7

Counts, N, were taken over four-minute periods for the various values of s with results as follows:

s/mm	10	15	30	45
N	too rapid for the counter	7820	7980	4536
s/mm	60	75	90	105
N	2942	2076	1554	1215

Copy this table adding further lines for n and $1/\sqrt{n}$, where n is the corrected count over four minutes (i.e. counts recorded minus background counts). It is thought that the relationship between n and s is likely to be of the form $1/\sqrt{n} = k(s + x)$, where k and x are constants. Plot a graph of $1/\sqrt{n}$ against s/mm, and use it to obtain values for k and x. What practical significance can be attached to x? Plot a further graph of $\lg n$ against $\lg((s + x)/\text{mm})$ and find its gradient.

(SUJB)

8. (1½ hours) Read the following account of an experimental investigation and then answer the questions at the end.
A thin metal wire is heated in a vacuum to a high temperature, T, by passing a steady current, I, through it. The potential difference, V, between the ends of the hot wire is also recorded. Varying I allows the wire to be heated to different temperatures.
At each temperature all the electrons which are emitted from the wire by thermionic emission are collected by a cylindrical metal anode surrounding the wire. The electrons constitute an emission

current, I_e, which is also recorded for each temperature of the wire.
The data obtained are tabulated below.

I/A	V/V	T/K	I_e/mA
2.01	5.00	1575	30.4
1.88	4.53	1545	16.9
1.74	3.95	1490	6.06
1.67	3.59	1445	2.95
1.52	3.06	1385	0.913
1.40	2.61	1320	0.234
1.34	2.34	1270	0.087

a) Assuming the variation of resistance with temperature for the material of the wire is given by
$R_T = R_0(1 + \alpha T + \beta T^2)$
where R_T is the resistance at temperature T and R_0, α and β are constants of the wire, show that a graph of $\dfrac{(R_T - R_0)}{T}$ as ordinate against T as abscissa should yield a linear plot.

b) Assuming $R_0 = 0.20\ \Omega$, construct a table of values of T, R_T and $(R_T - R_0)/T$. By plotting a graph of $(R_T - R_0)/T$ as ordinate against T as abscissa, determine the value of α and β.

c) It is suspected that over the range of temperatures used, the emission current, I_e, is related to the temperature, T, of the wire by the relation
$I_e = cT^n$
where c and n are constants.
By plotting a graph of $\log_{10}(I_e/\text{mA})$ as ordinate against $\log_{10}(T/K)$ as abscissa test this relation, and hence deduce a value for n.

d) It was hoped to stabilize the temperature of the wire at 1520 K, but this could only be achieved to ±1%.
(i) What are the maximum and minimum temperatures of the wire for this 1% variation?
(ii) Find, using your graph in question c) above or otherwise, the corresponding maximum and minimum emission currents.

(London)

6 In the laboratory

The role of measurements

Physics is an experimental science. Our present understanding of the natural world is based on theories and principles that have been tested by experiments. Theories which do not fit the facts obtained by experiments must be discarded or adapted. New discoveries by experimenters test existing theories; if the theory fails the test, its basic assumptions must be questioned. Science is littered with discarded ideas once held high as being correct; the 'caloric theory' is one such example. Heat was thought of as a fluid that flowed from hot to cold objects. Benjamin Thompson put paid to 'caloric' in the early 19th century when he showed that doing work by drilling on a metal caused it to heat up.

What do we mean when we say a theory is 'correct'? Essentially, the meaning is that no one has managed to disprove it. All the experimental tests on that theory have confirmed its correctness; if any one test had disagreed with the theory, then the theory must be adapted or replaced. We can never say that a given theory is 'true' because someone, somewhere, might manage to disprove it as a result of a new experiment. Science works by disproving ideas and theories; our understanding of the natural world is in terms of ideas and theories that have not been disproved.

A famous example of the link between theory and experiment is the so-called **ultra-violet catastrophe** of the late 19th century. Up to that time, light was believed to travel in the form of continuous waves emitted by light sources. Wave theory successfully explained interference and diffraction effects. However, in the late 19th century, two experimenters, O. Lummer and E. Pringsheim, carried out a detailed investigation of the thermal radiation from 'black body radiators'. They measured the distribution of radiation energy with wavelength for the black body at different temperatures. Their results in graph form are known as black body radiation curves (see Fig 6.1); these curves presented the best scientists of that time with more than a headache! Wave theory could be used to explain the curve either side of the peak, but it predicted an infinitely high peak. The problem became known as the 'ultra-violet catastrophe' because the unwanted infinity was towards the UV region of the electromagnetic spectrum. Eventually, the problem was solved by Planck and Einstein, who rethought the nature of light and established the photon theory of light. Black body radiation curves are explained with complete success using the photon theory. And the photon theory predicts and explains much more too.

Experimental work in physics involves testing theories by investigating relationships between physical quantities. An equally important role for the experimenter is to investigate the behaviour of materials and devices. Once known, the material or device can be used correctly within its known limitations. If the behaviour is not fully known, the device or material could fail, with disastrous results! So experimenters have a dual role. Theories must be tested and materials and devices must be investigated. The first aspect, testing theories, is essentially pure science; testing materials and devices involves applications of science although there is often no well-defined border between applied and pure science. Both aspects involve identifying, controlling and measuring physical quantities, then looking for links between the quantities.

Measurements play a key role in science, so they must be reliable. Reliability means that a consistent value should be obtained each time the same measurement is repeated. An unreliable weighing machine in a shop would make the customers go elsewhere. In science, you can't go elsewhere so the measurements must be reliable. Each time a given measurement is repeated, it should give the same value within acceptable limits. What do we mean by acceptable limits? Consider the example of measuring the diameter of a uniform wire using a micrometer. Suppose the following readings are taken for different positions along the wire from one end to the other, diameter d: 0.34 mm 0.33 mm 0.36 mm 0.33 mm 0.35 mm.

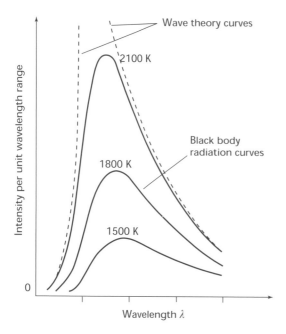

Fig 6.1 The ultra-violet catastrophe

The mean value, d̄ (sometimes written $<d>$) is 0.34 mm, calculated by adding the readings together and dividing by the number of readings.

If the difference between each reading and d̄ changed regularly from one end of the wire to the other, then it would be reasonable to conclude that the wire was non-uniform. The differences would be called 'systematic'. No such differences can be seen in the above set of readings. In other words, there is no pattern obvious, so the differences are random. Random differences may be due to the observer's judgement, the instrument or the non-uniformity of the wire. The spread of readings is from 0.33 to 0.36 mm, and most of them lie within 0.1 mm of the mean value. So the diameter is 0.34 ± 0.1 mm. The ± 0.1 mm is called the **probable error** of the value. Statistics formulae can be used to calculate probable errors.

Measuring instruments

Achieving accuracy

Instruments used in the physics laboratory range from very basic (e.g. a mm scale) to the highly-sophisticated (e.g. multi-channel data recorders). Whatever type of instruments you use, you need to be aware of the following key points.

Zero error Does the instrument read zero when it is supposed to? For example, voltmeters and ammeters need to be checked before use to ensure they read zero when disconnected. Another example is using a micrometer; when the measuring gap is closed, the reading ought to be zero. If not, the zero reading must be taken into account when measuring the gap width.

Sensitivity In general terms, sensitivity is the reading per unit 'input'. For example, if the sensitivity of a microammeter is given as 75 mm μA^{-1}; then the meaning is that the reading in mm is $75 \times$ the current in μA. An instrument that becomes less sensitive with age will give readings that are consistently low, causing systematic errors. Multi-range meters can be set for different ranges according to the situation. Each range has a different sensitivity. For example, when a multi-range voltmeter is used, the correct range to use is the one that gives the biggest reading on the meter scale without overloading the scale. Another example is when an oscilloscope is used to display a wave form; the Y-gain is adjusted to make the wave form cover as much as possible of the screen without any part of it disappearing off the screen.

Linearity is a design feature of most instruments. An instrument is 'linear' if its reading is proportional to the quantity being measured. So the sensitivity (= reading per unit quantity) is constant if the instrument is linear. For example, suppose a voltmeter which is linear is checked using a standard 1.08 V cell.

- The zero reading is checked first.
- The standard cell is connected to the meter, and the reading should be 1.08V.
- For measuring other voltages, the reading is proportional to the voltage since the meter is linear. So if the voltmeter gives a reading that is $0.5 \times$ the reading for 1.08 V, then the voltage is 0.54 V. To check linearity, the instrument must be recalibrated over the whole of its range.

Accuracy is only possible if there are no systematic errors when a measurement is made. Precise readings are not necessarily accurate readings, since systematic errors could make precise readings lower than they ought to be. For example, suppose the hairsprings of a certain moving coil meter have become weaker with age; precise readings can still be made from the scale but they would be consistently greater than the correct readings since the coil becomes easier to deflect. So the readings would not be accurate.

The accuracy of a measurement is given by the probable error or the percentage error. By making several readings for a given measurement, the probable error can be estimated from the spread of readings; if all the readings are the same, the probable error is given by the precision of reading the scale. The same applies if just one reading is made. Figure 6.2 shows the scale of an ammeter where a reading is to be made. What do you think the reading is? How precise is the reading? You could use a lens as a magnifying glass to make it even more precise.

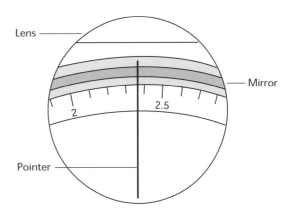

Fig 6.2 Magnifying a scale

Accuracy is easy to lose, even with simple equipment. For example, when investigating free fall, the metre rule must be vertical. To check that this is so, a plumb line is used, made of a string supporting a mass at rest. If the metre rule appears parallel to the plumb line from the front **and** the side, the rule is then vertical.

Precision can be lost through lack of care in reading the position of a pointer against a scale. The line of sight from the observer to the pointer must be at right angles to the scale. A plane mirror behind the scale is helpful. The observer reads the

47

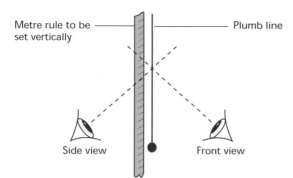

Fig 6.3 Finding the vertical

Metre rule to be set vertically — Plumb line

Side view — Front view

If the metre rule appears parallel to the plumb line from the front and the side, the rule must be vertical

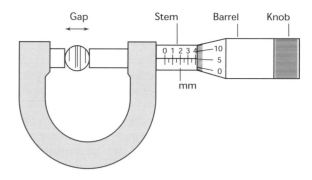

Fig 6.5 Using a micrometer

Gap   Stem   Barrel   Knob

mm

scale when the pointer's image is directly behind the pointer, so the scale is observed correctly. See Fig 6.4.

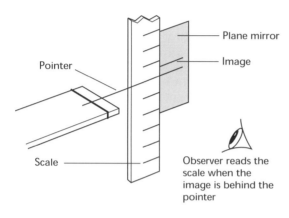

Plane mirror

Image

Pointer

Scale

Observer reads the scale when the image is behind the pointer

Fig 6.4 Reading a scale

Micrometers and verniers

Micrometers give readings with a precision of 0.01 mm. The barrel of a micrometer is a screw with a pitch of 0.5 mm. The edge of the barrel is marked in 50 equal intervals so each interval corresponds to changing the gap of the micrometer by $0.5/50 = 0.01$ mm. The stem of the micrometer is marked with a linear scale graduated in $\frac{1}{2}$ mm intervals.

With the gap closed, the zero mark on the barrel scale should be exactly against the zero mark on the linear scale. When the gap is opened, its width is given by where the readings on the scales intersect. Figure 6.5 shows a reading of 4.56mm. To use a micrometer correctly:

- check its zero reading,
- open the gap by turning the barrel, then close the gap on the object to be measured. Turn the knob until it slips or clicks, when the gap is closed. Don't overtighten the barrel. Take the reading, and calculate the gap width from the two readings. The accuracy of the measurement is ±0.01 mm because each reading is accurate to ±0.005 mm, and the difference between

readings is accurate to the sum of the individual errors.

Vernier calipers can be used for measurements of distances up to 100 mm, or more. The precision is not as great as with a micrometer since vernier readings are accurate to ±0.05 mm. However, vernier calipers are more versatile as they can be used for internal and external measurements.

The sliding scale of any vernier has ten equal intervals covering an exact distance of 9 mm, so each interval on the sliding scale is 0.1 mm less than a 1mm interval. To make a reading, the zero mark on the sliding scale is used to read the main scale to the nearest millimetre. This reading is rounded down to the nearest mm. Then the sliding scale is inspected, using a lens as a magnifying glass if necessary. The number of the mark on the sliding scale closest to a mark on the main scale is noted. This number ×0.1 mm is the amount the zero reading was rounded down by. Figure 6.6 shows the idea; the 5th mark after the zero on the sliding scale is in line with a mm mark on the main scale. So the distance from the 39 mm mark on the main scale and the sliding scale zero is 0.5 mm. Hence the vernier reading is 39.5 mm. As with a micrometer, the zero reading should be checked and taken into account if necessary.

Micrometers or verniers rarely need recalibrating. Thermal expansion is negligible over the range of temperatures that they are likely to be subjected

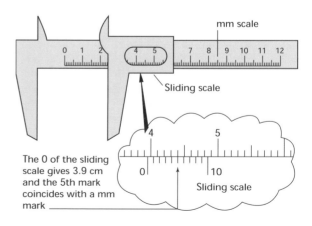

mm scale

Sliding scale

The 0 of the sliding scale gives 3.9 cm and the 5th mark coincides with a mm mark

Sliding scale

Fig 6.6 Using a vernier

to, although the instruments can become worn if used carelessly.

Timing

Stopwatches used for interval timing are subject to human error because reaction time, about 0.2 s, is variable for any individual. Starting and stopping a stopwatch involves similar delays at the start and finish, but even so, precision of less than 0.1 s is not likely because of random error. Digital stopwatches can give read-outs precise to within ±0.01 s. But unless they are operated from electronic gates, human error makes read-outs to ±0.01 s meaningless, and the reading must be considered accurate to ±0.1 s at most.

Timing oscillations requires timing for as many cycles as possible. The timing should be repeated several times to give an average value. Any timing that is significantly different to the other values is probably due to miscounting, so that timing is rejected. For example, suppose the timings for a given simple pendulum are as follows:

Time for 20 complete cycles/s: 20.1 19.8 19.7 20.2 20.0 18.3 19.8 20.4.

The timing of 18.3 s is rejected because it was probably due to miscounting. The mean value is then 20.0 s with a spread from 19.7 to 20.4 s. Most of the readings lie in the range from 19.8 to 20.2 s so the timing is 20.0 ± 0.2 s.

For accurate timing of oscillations, a **fiducial mark** is essential. The mark acts as reference to count the number of cycles as the object swings past each cycle.

Electronic timers use gates to start and stop an electronic counter. The counter is supplied with 1.0 kHz pulses when the 'condition' of the gates allows. So the counter read-out is precise to 1 ms (i.e. 1 pulse). Figure 6.7 shows a single light gate to time a card attached to a trolley as the trolley passes under the gate. When the card interrupts the light beam, the counter operates, so the counter read-out gives the time in ms for the card to pass through the gate. Suppose the timing was repeated several times, each time the trolley being released from rest at the same point. The probable error is estimated from the spread of the readings; if the readings are all the same (unlikely in this situation), then

10 kHz pulses should be used so that the read-out is more precise.

Another method of using electronic timers is to allow one gate to switch the counter on and then a different gate to switch it off. For example, a falling object could be timed over a measured distance in this way.

Light gates can be interfaced to a microcomputer to use the micro's internal clock. The microcomputer must be programmed to start timing when it receives a signal from the light gate, and then to stop when a second signal is received. The program must include the instruction to print the timing on the VDU screen, and usually a calculation in the program is necessary to give the timing in seconds.

Checking the accuracy of a timer can be done using a time signal from the radio or 'phone to start the timer. Then a second time signal is used to stop the timer. For example, suppose a stopwatch is allowed to run for 30 minutes exactly, and when it is stopped it shows a reading of 30 min 10s. The stopwatch has 'gained' 10 s in 30 minutes so each stopwatch second is $\frac{1800}{1810}$ s. Timing using this stopwatch needs to be corrected for systematic error.

Top-pan balances

Electronic balances for measuring mass usually give digital read-outs. Before using a top-pan balance, its zero reading must be checked and taken into account if necessary. Top-pan balances need to be checked for accuracy at regular intervals; a set of standard masses is essential for this purpose. Use tweezers to lift standard masses to prevent any deposit or corrosion that might be caused if the masses are handled.

Voltmeters and ammeters

Whether digital or analogue (i.e. pointer-type), electrical meters should be checked for accuracy at regular intervals and recalibrated if necessary.

Voltmeters can be calibrated using a potentiometer and a standard cell. Figure 6.8 shows a suitable circuit for this purpose. The potentiometer wire is

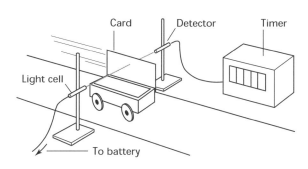

Fig 6.7 Electronic timing

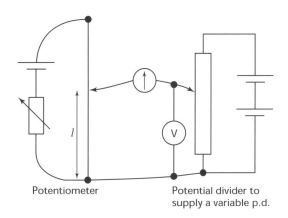

Fig 6.8 Calibrating a voltmeter

calibrated using a standard cell. Then the voltmeter reading is adjusted in steps to different values. At each value, the balance point on the wire is located and the balance length l is measured. Then the correct p.d. across the voltmeter is calculated from

$$V = \frac{\text{standard e.m.f.}}{\text{standard balance length}} \times l$$

A calibration curve of calculated p.d. against voltmeter readings is a convenient way to display and use the results.

If the range of the voltmeter is beyond the range of p.d.s from the potentiometer, then the circuit is modified. Figure 6.9 shows the modification; two accurate resistance boxes in series are connected across the voltmeter terminals. By setting the resistance boxes at known values, a known fraction of the voltmeter p.d. is dropped across each box. The potentiometer p.d. is balanced against the p.d. across one of the boxes. The potentiometer p.d. is equal to $VR_2/(R_1 + R_2)$ where V is the voltmeter reading, and R_1 and R_2 are the box resistances as in Fig 6.9.

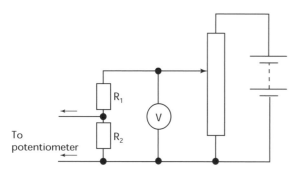

Fig 6.9 Extending the range

Ammeters can be calibrated or checked by connecting the meter in series with a standard resistor. A potentiometer is then used to measure the p.d. across the standard resistor. Figure 6.10 shows the arrangement. The current is then calculated from the measured p.d./resistance of the standard resistor. The calculated value is compared with the measured value of current. By making measure-

ments at steps over the ammeter's range, a calibration curve can be drawn, as shown in Fig 6.11. The curve can then be used to determine the correct current for a given ammeter reading if there is a difference.

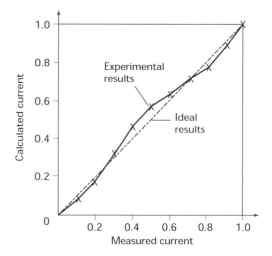

Fig. 6.11 A calibration curve

Oscilloscopes

Oscilloscopes are used to measure p.d.s and time intervals. To check its accuracy for p.d.s, the same method as for a voltmeter can be used; in theory, the vertical deflection of the trace on the screen is proportional to the input p.d. To check the Y-gain sensitivity, the deflection of the trace is measured for a given input p.d. from a standard cell or potentiometer. The sensitivity is equal to the deflection/input p.d.

To check the accuracy for timing intervals, a signal of known frequency (e.g. 50 Hz) is applied to the Y-input; with the time-base on, a stable wave form is displayed on the screen. The time period of the signal (= 1/frequency of the signal) is then used to check the time-base setting; this is done by measuring the distance across the screen for one complete cycle. This distance × the time-base setting (in ms cm^{-1} for example) gives the time period measurement.

Projects and investigations

Short experiments

You have probably done lots of short experiments in your physics classes by now. Some short experiments might require more than the usual 1 to 2 hour laboratory session but in general, short experiments are usually done in a single session. Short experiments generally involve one or more of the following tasks.

- Practising a particular skill (e.g. using an oscilloscope for measuring).

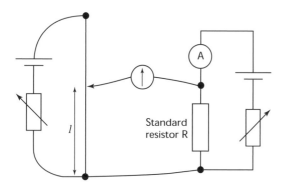

Fig 6.10 Calibrating an ammeter

- Measuring some property of a material (e.g. the density of a solid).
- Determining the characteristics of a device (e.g. a transistor).
- Testing a suspected link between two physical quantities.

Usually a short experiment involves carrying out specific tasks by following a set of instructions. The instructions might tell you which variables to control and which to measure. You may need to select suitable instruments for the measurements from a range of instruments available. You might need to select the most suitable range for an instrument.

Consider the example of using the ammeter-voltmeter method to measure the resistance of a wirewound resistor. Suppose you are given a suitable voltmeter, a multimeter, a variable resistor and a 6 V battery and switch. Your instructions might be as follows.

Use the equipment given to measure the current through resistor X for several different values of p.d. across X up to 6 V. Plot a graph of your results, and use the graph to calculate the resistance of X.

STEP 1 Sketch the circuit diagram you propose to use.

STEP 2 Make out a table for your results.

STEP 3 Connect the circuit together but keep the switch open. Check the zero readings on the meters. Set the multimeter range switch for maximum d.c. current.

STEP 4 Close the switch and check that the current can be varied by altering the variable resistor. For maximum current, set the multimeter range switch to give the maximum on-scale reading.

STEP 5 Alter the p.d. in regular steps. At each step, measure the p.d. using the voltmeter and measure the current using the multimeter. Note the probable error for each meter. Open the switch but don't disconnect the circuit. More readings may need to be made.

STEP 6 Plot p.d. against current, including the zero readings. For each point, outline its error box as in Fig 5.3. Then determine the resistance from the maximum and minimum gradient. If the steepest line through the error boxes gives 6.3 ohms, and the least steep line gives 5.9 ohms, then the resistance of X is 6.1 ± 0.2 ohms.

Whatever the experiment, the procedure is along the lines indicated. If the instructions are brief, as in the example above, then you need to plan the procedure step-by-step. You may find it is helpful to write your account of the experiment as you proceed with the experiment.

Title e.g. 'Measurement of the resistance of a wire wound resistor by the ammeter-voltmeter method'.

Diagram e.g. circuit diagram, labelled with the range of the meters shown.

Method e.g. write up details as in Steps 4, 5 and 6.

Results e.g. the table of measurements.

Treatment of results e.g. a brief explanation of relevant theory, leading to the chosen graph.

Graph e.g. as in Step 6.

Calculations e.g. as in Step 6.

Conclusions give the value of resistance, and comment on accuracy.

Short investigations

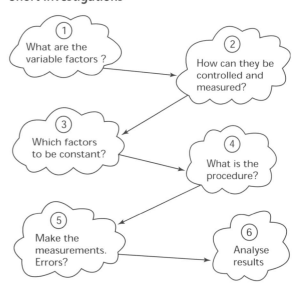

Fig 6.12 Short investigations

Investigations involve decisions being made by the experimenter. What are the variable quantities involved? Which one should be controlled to measure its effect on other quantities? What method should be used? These are all questions you need to ask yourself before you start using any apparatus. For example, suppose you are asked to investigate the factors that determine the fundamental frequency of vibration of a given wire. You might suspect the factors include the vibrating length, the tension and the amplitude of vibration. You could vary each factor in turn, keeping the other ones constant, to discover the effect of each factor individually on the frequency of vibration. You could choose the a.c. sonometer method (see textbook p. 330) for this experiment. Then you need to decide on the procedure step by step.

STEP 1 List the factors that you think affect the frequency. Consider and note how each factor can be varied.
Tension: use different load weights.
Length: use a movable bridge to alter the vibrating length.

Amplitude: change the amplitude of the alternating current in the wire.

STEP 2 How can you measure the frequency and the other factors? Note briefly the instrument and procedure for each factor.

Frequency: use a frequency meter connected across the output terminals of the signal generator.

Tension: use a top pan balance to measure the mass of each of the load weights if necessary.

Length: use a mm scale.

Amplitude: use an a.c. ammeter in series with the wire.

STEP 3 Choose one of the factors to vary and keep the other two factors constant. Alter the chosen variable in steps, and at each step adjust the frequency until the wire resonates in its fundamental mode. Check that the other factors (tension and current if the length is the chosen variable) remain unchanged. Then measure the frequency and the chosen variable. Repeat for different values of the chosen variable. Note the measurements in table form, and note the probable errors.

STEP 4 If you suspect a link between the frequency and the chosen variable, plot a graph to give a straight line. For example, if you suspect that the frequency is proportional to 1/length, then plot frequency against 1/length. A straight line confirms your suspected link.

A better approach to establish a link is to plot a log-log graph. The idea of log-log graphs is explained on p. 28. Suppose the link is in the form

$f = kx^n$

where x is the variable factor,
f is the frequency
k is a constant.

The power n is to be determined to establish the link.

$\log f = n \log x + \log k$

Hence a graph of $\log f$ against $\log x$ should give a straight line with gradient n if the link is of the form $f = kx^n$. If the graph does give a straight line, then the value of n can be determined.

STEP 5 Summarize any links you have established. In this example, the frequency is:

- proportional to 1/length.
- proportional to √tension.
- independent of amplitude.

Longer investigations and projects

The skills and methods used in short investigations are important in any long investigation or project.

But other techniques and skills are important too. Short investigations are usually carried out with a limited aim in mind (e.g. measure the density, etc., investigate the variation of, etc.) so you start with that aim in mind. Longer investigations are often open-ended so you cannot predict where the investigation will lead when you start. If you start with a vague, general aim in mind, you may find difficulty in deciding the direction to take; there might be too many variables to sort out. So if you are choosing a project, you should not be too ambitious to involve too many factors.

With a suitable investigation chosen, now you need to organize yourself. No set instructions can cover a project so start by deciding on the general procedure to follow. If necessary, buy a note book with alternate graph and lined pages. The note book is useful as a diary in which to plan your project. You can use it to record your thoughts, decisions, ideas on design etc., as you proceed with the project. Measurements, errors, theory, graphs and calculations should all be included in your note book. Here are some hints to help you get organized.

1 Research the topic area by selective reading from your text book and any other suitable books. Note down any promising 'lines' of investigation and any potential difficulties.

2 Narrow the area of interest down to an investigation with just a few variables involved. Make sure that you have the facilities to control and measure the variables. Perhaps a little more reading-up is necessary here. Check that your teacher thinks your project is feasible in the time available.

3 Note the variables you intend to measure or control. Plan to operate on a 'cause and effect' basis with one variable being changed causing another variable to alter; the other variables need to be monitored to make sure they do not change.

4 List the equipment necessary for your measurements, etc. Check it is available when you wish to use it. List all the materials and components required. If necessary, obtain materials from home or a local supplier.

5 Design, construct and test any special pieces of equipment you need for your measurements.

6 Modify your plans or designs as a result of preliminary tests.

Let's see how this procedure might work in practice. Suppose you wish to investigate the friction and slipperiness of floor coverings used in kitchens.

Researching should enable you to discover that friction between solid surfaces is measured by the coefficient of friction μ. So your investigation narrows down to measuring μ for different surfaces. The surfaces need to be clean and dry to test for maximum friction.

Measurements to determine the coefficient of friction need to be considered next. μ is defined as the frictional force at the point of slipping/the normal reaction at the surface. On a level surface, the normal reaction is equal to the force pressing down. So the frictional force at the point of slipping must be measured for different loadings on the surfaces (assumed level).

Equipment and design is the next step. A top-pan balance is needed to measure the load weights. A spring balance or an uncalibrated spring as a forcemeter is needed to measure the frictional force at the point of slipping. To apply a gradually increasing frictional force, a 'test-rig' along the lines of Fig 6.13 must be designed. One of the surfaces to be tested is fixed on the bed of the test rig. The other surface is stuck onto the lower surface of the test box. The box is to be loaded with different weights. For each load weight, the forcemeter is used to apply a gradually increasing force until the box slips. The reading of the forcemeter, just on the point of slipping, is equal to the frictional force. Modify the design if necessary to detect the point of slipping more accurately.

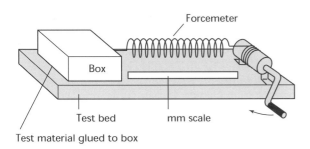

Figure 6.13 A test rig

Calibrate the forcemeter by suspending known weights from it when it is held vertical. Plot a calibration graph of tension against extension. Now follow the same general steps as for any short investigation.

STEP 1 Obtain sets of readings of the frictional force F and load weight W, using fresh samples of the same material. Note the errors involved in your measurements.

STEP 2 Plot graphs F against W to determine μ for each sample from the gradient of the line. Hence obtain an average value of μ for the pair of materials under test.

STEP 3 Repeat the procedure for other materials used as the surface of the test bed but keep the same material on the box throughout. In this way, the values of μ measure the friction between a given material as a 'shoe' and different floor surfaces.

Conclusions from your results must be justified by the results. For example, measuring μ for two different floor coverings might give the result that μ for floorcovering X is greater than μ for floorcovering Y. But you need to consider the probable error of each value. If $\mu_X = 0.55 \pm 0.10$ and $\mu_Y = 0.48 \pm 0.08$, then you would not be justified in claiming μ_X is greater than μ_Y. You would need to test more samples of X and Y and you would need to improve the less accurate features of the experiment. If time does not permit further investigations, then you should outline in your conclusions what further investigations you would have done.

Writing a report on your investigation is an important part of the work in itself. The note book should contain all the day-to-day details of the project; planning, organization, decision making, design details, measurements, errors, graphs, calculations should all be in the note book. The book might cover 50 or more pages, and its details are vital for your report. But the report itself should be based on **selective** use of your note book. Details of abandoned ideas would not be an essential part of your report, so only a brief reason need be given in your report to explain why you changed your ideas or approach. Your note book might contain lots of tables of measurements; these can be given as an appendix to your report. Report writing is discussed in more detail on p. 54–56. Don't neglect this important aspect of any project; your experimental skills might be 'honed to perfection' but if your report is ill-prepared, the reader will probably fail to appreciate your skills. It's a bit like a superb footballer who forgets which end to attack – and scores an own goal!

The written report

Explaining yourself

Scientists need to communicate their ideas to one another and to the general public. Sometimes the writers of scientific articles in popular magazines forget the intended reader and write as if to another scientist. Then the unfortunate reader is left to struggle with the article. Sometimes the writer 'waters down' the scientific content to a trivial level, and the reader gains little from the article. It is not just scientists who make this sort of mistake though: Inland Revenue returns can be taxing in more ways than one! Here are some simple rules.

- Use short words if possible.
- Use familiar words if possible.
- Avoid 'padding' with unnecessary words.
- Avoid long sentences if possible.

Perhaps you have met someone who deliberately breaks the rules. Don't be impressed! Pompous expressions might make the user feel terribly clever and superior, but anyone who resorts to such expressions is probably hiding his or her lack of knowledge. Communicating ideas is too important to allow barriers to be erected. Physics is a subject with lots of difficult ideas; no one gains if the subject is expressed in ways that make it seem more difficult. Your studies in science would be incomplete if you were unable to express your ideas effectively.

Technical terms are terms that have a special meaning in the context in which they are used. For example, 'coherence' has a special meaning when it is used in physics. Its general meaning is 'holding together'; its use in physics extends that meaning to waves with a constant phase difference. Scientists often use technical terms without explanation when communicating with each other; sometimes an unfamiliar technical term needs explaining. Usually though, the user assumes the reader or listener is familiar with the term. The writer must judge which technical terms need explaining. Too many explanations would interrupt the train of thought of the reader; too few explanations would make the reader stumble along, unable to develop a train of thought.

Where a technical term is introduced and explained, it can then be used subsequently without explanation. The more often the term is used after being introduced, the more familiar the reader becomes with that term. But if several terms are introduced and explained close together, then the reader can become confused.

When writing a scientific article, the writer must keep the scientific background of the typical reader in mind.

- Specialists in the same subject would need newly-discovered ideas and methods to be explained. A survey of knowledge up to the point of discovery is helpful. But unnecessary explanations of specialist terms would hide the impact of the discovery.
- If intended for non-specialists with a scientific background, then the specialist terms would need to be explained. For example, suppose you were to read an article about Astronomy, and you met the unit 'the parsec' without an explanation. Your progress would be halted whilst you thought about its meaning, and you might need to consult a reference book. So a brief explanation, perhaps in a separate diagram, would be more than helpful. However, with a scientific background, you ought to be familiar with SI units, prefixes, use of formulae, graphs and general scientific terms. In other words, 'scientific literacy' is assumed.
- For intended readers who are not scientists, only a limited scientific background can be assumed. For example, an article about 'World Fuel Supplies' might perhaps include a paragraph or two about energy transformations. The article might discuss chemical energy, heat energy, nuclear energy and electrical energy; but the writer would probably assume that the reader is aware that there are other forms of energy.

Essays and essay-style answers written in physics examinations need careful planning. The intended reader is either your teacher (for internal exams) or a distant examiner; so your reader is a highly-qualified scientist whose task is to assess your knowledge and understanding of the topic in question. The purpose of your answer is not to enlighten the reader, but to demonstrate your knowledge. Suppose you don't explain your ideas fully because you think the examiner is bound to know what you mean anyway. The examiner can only judge what you have written so will assume that you cannot understand the ideas. 'But I meant ⋯' may keep your teacher happy, but your examiner judges only what is on paper.

So what should be your approach? As a useful guide, write your answer as if for a classmate who missed the topic. You can then assume a scientific background, but you must explain technical terms relevant to that topic.

Many essay questions provide little information and expect you to write your answer with little guidance from the question. For example:

This question is about explaining ideas. Give a

careful explanation of the topics listed, as if for a classmate who missed the subject.

Subject *Digital electronics*

Topics in the subject *Logic levels, logic gates, flip-flops, indicators.*

An answer plan is essential; start by listing relevant points against each topic heading. Then link the sub-topics together. Then decide the order you think best for the points in your answer. When you write out your answer, don't forget that labelled diagrams save lots of unnecessary writing; you need only refer to key features of the diagrams in your written answer. A possible answer plan is shown in Fig 7.1.

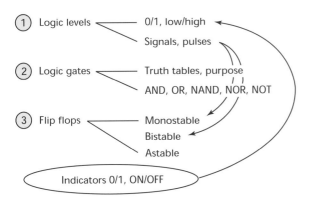

Fig 7.1 Answer plan

Project reports

Planning your report

Before you start writing a report about a project or investigation, your first step should be to make up a 'plan of attack'. Your report will be based on the information in your project note book; all the day-by-day details should be in the note book. Your plan could take the form of the main headings you intend to use in your report, with important points jotted down under each heading. If you restrict your plan to a single side of paper, then you can spot anything left out of the plan. The plan then

1. Project outline
2. Theory
3. Procedure
4. Results
5. Treatment of results
6. Errors
7. Conclusion

Fig 7.2 Report plan

gives you an overall framework that will guide you through the actual writing of the report. (See Fig 7.2).

The main headings, in order, would probably be as follows:

1 Project outline or 'abstract' At the start of your report, after the title, give an outline of the project in no more than half a page or so. The outline should state the aim of the project, and the general method used to achieve your aim. If the aim is in general terms (e.g. to investigate methods of preventing 'thermal runaway' of transistors), then more precise details should be given. In addition, a brief explanation of specialist terms (like 'thermal runaway' in the above example) should be given.

2 Theory Explain what quantities you intend to control and measure. Give the theory that shows how the measurements relate to your aim.

3 Apparatus Describe, with the aid of labelled diagrams, the apparatus you used. Number your diagrams (e.g. *Figure 1*) so you can refer to them in your writing. Include details of any equipment you designed, tested and used. If you changed the apparatus during the project, state why the change was necessary.

4 Procedure The next step is to describe how you used the apparatus. How did you control and measure the variable quantities? List the sequence in which the measurements were made. List the instruments used for each measurement. What steps did you take to check the consistency of your readings? Refer to diagrams and tables of measurements by number. How did you estimate the probable errors in your measurements? List the precautions taken to ensure consistent and accurate readings.

5 Results Give your measurements in the order you took them in. Tabulate sets of measurements and number each table. If your measurements take up more than a page or so, plan them as an 'appendix' to the report, and refer to the tables in the results section. List units and probable errors.

6 Treatment of results

- Calculations from the measurements and related theory are to be given here. For calculations on a set of measurements, give the results in a table.
- Graphs to be plotted are listed here, with a brief explanation of why you have chosen each graph. Each graph can be given in an appendix with a reference number. Calculation of gradients and intercepts of straight lines can be given on the graph sheets, but state the results of your calculations in the main report. Explain how you measured the gradient of any curves. Show probable errors and gradient triangles on the graphs, but comment on the features of the graph in the main report.

- Final calculations should include any theory necessary to explain your use of previous calculations or data from measurements or graphs. In other words, if your final calculation draws data from different parts of your report, explain the theory behind the calculations.

7 Accuracy and errors The measurements and graphs ought to show probable errors. Describe the steps you took to eliminate systematic errors (e.g. calibrating meters) and random errors (e.g. repeating readings). Then show how the errors are treated in the final calculations to give the total error.

8 Conclusions State the results of your final calculations, including your estimate of the total error. Comment on any unusually large errors in the measurements, and suggest ways to reduce any such errors.

State any mathematical links between quantities established or confirmed by your project. Discuss how well you have achieved your initial aim; be critical here, and don't claim without justification. Describe further tests you could have done or improvements you would have made if more time had been available.

Style and presentation

The style and presentation of your report are important. Aim to make your report easy to follow. The layout should include clear, numbered headings. Tables of measurements and diagrams should be clearly set out, numbered and given a caption (e.g. *Figure 1 The test rig*). If there are lots of measurements to report, keep them in a separate appendix after the main report; in this way, the flow of your report is not broken by pages of measurements. You can then refer to any table by its reference number. Avoid the need for the reader to jump forward or refer back to key sections of the report; a brief quote from the key section is preferable.

A plain style of writing allows the scientific content to stand out. Think about the words you choose so you can avoid lapses like '... the thermometer rose by ...'. Be precise when you explain how a measurement was made: '... the time taken for 20 oscillations was measured.' What was used for the timing? Was a fiducial mark used? Why were 20 oscillations timed? The report should tell the reader how you made the measurements, not just what the measurements were. 'The wave form was measured ...'. does not convey what aspect of the wave form was measured, so more information is needed.

A useful idea is to prepare a draft report and ask a friend to read it through; your friend may pinpoint phrases where the meaning is not clear or where there is insufficient explanation.

 Comprehension

Reading skills need to be developed, like any other form of skills. Background reading is one way to further your reading skills; choose articles that interest you from popular scientific magazines or from 'Science Extra' features in newspapers.

If an article is particularly relevant to your studies, write a summary of it to include with your notes. Reading articles in this way should help you to develop your writing skills too!

What sort of skills are involved in effective reading? The aim of reading a scientific article is to absorb information or to develop understanding. If an article is entertaining too, then so much the better. It's useful to mark long articles into sections, to be read through section by section.

STEP 1 Read each section at your normal reading speed without 'backtracking'. As you read through, mark any unfamiliar terms and underline any points you consider important.

STEP 2 Now consider the unfamiliar terms one by one; make sure that you know the meaning of each. If necessary, refer to your text book although a well-written article ought to explain unfamiliar terms.

STEP 3 Re-read the section critically, looking for links between key points.

Reading is more effective if you think for yourself as you read through. A scientific article is meant to convey knowledge; you should ask yourself what you have gained in knowledge through reading the article. Has the article widened your scientific background or developed your understanding? If not, you might as well have read a short story! Sharpen your reading skills and your studies in science will become much more effective.

Examination questions can easily be misread under pressure in an examination room. Missing the point of an article or question is all too easy when under strain. So you need to practise your reading skills alongside laboratory skills, mathematical skills, etc. All too often, candidates answer the question they had hoped for rather than the one actually asked. If the topic in a question is seen as its key feature, then the instructions may be misread. Consider the following example:

Describe the motion of smoke particles in air when viewed using a microscope.

If you write all about air molecules moving at random, you have missed the point of the question. The question asks you to **describe** the motion of the smoke particles, not to say what you think is the cause of their motion. If the question had read '*Describe and explain ...*'

Comprehension papers and longer examination questions are scientific articles so the skills mentioned above are important. A typical comprehension paper develops a topic in the syllabus by introducing and using unfamiliar ideas. The passage explains such ideas so you have to take the meaning in. What's the best way to do this? Use the same sort of approach as for any scientific article – as described earlier. Here's a summary:

STEP 1 Read the passage through and mark unfamiliar terms.

STEP 2 Look for the meaning of these terms in the passage.

STEP 3 Then re-read the passage before tackling the questions.

Usually, the questions follow the paragraphs in sequence. As you come to each question, identify which part of the passage the question is drawn from, and re-read that section before you attempt your answer. If necessary, jot the key points of your answer down on rough paper and link them together in an answer plan; base your answer on the plan.

The questions in a typical comprehension paper test a wide range of skills. Your reading skills are obviously under test. But so too are your skills of writing, graph work, calculation and so on. You may be asked to explain an unfamiliar term in your own words; or you may be asked to use an unfamiliar formula given in the passage. You could be asked to plot a graph based on the formula. You will undoubtedly be asked to show your knowledge of physics, and perhaps to apply that knowledge to an unfamiliar situation. It is a good idea to practise doing comprehension papers and longer questions to help you develop your skills of physics. Even if you do not pursue your studies in physics beyond your present course, the skills you develop will help you in any career. That's why physics students are sought after by such a wide range of employers!

8 | Using IT in physics

There are many opportunities to use IT in one form or another in an AS level or Advanced level Physics course. You can use IT in the laboratory to take measurements and to analyse data. You can use IT to prepare a coursework report, taking advantage of opportunities to import graphs and charts into it. You can use IT to develop your grasp of difficult ideas using visual displays from CD-ROMs or using spreadsheets to work out changes. In addition, you can use IT to find out the latest scientific developments and you can e-mail scientists in any country if you need help with a project. If used sensibly, IT can help you to improve your knowledge and understanding of physics as well as helping you with making measurements in the laboratory. However, make sure you use IT for a specific purpose and ensure that there is a definite advantage to be gained by its use each time you use it. Here are some notes to help you to decide when to use IT on your physics course. The following notes apply to any software package and do not attempt to teach you the intricacies of a particular software package.

Data logging enables routine measurements to be made as well as measurements over very long or very short time scales. For example, you could use an ammeter sensor and a data logger to find out how the current through a filament light bulb changes when the light bulb is switched on. Most data loggers can make thousands of measurements in less than a second and then display the measurements on a screen or an oscilloscope. On a longer time scale, a data logger can be used to make measurements over several days, for example to find out how the temperature of a building changes over a period of a few days. Routine measurements can be boring so a data logger is ideal for making such measurements while you concentrate on much more important matters. For example, a temperature sensor linked to a data logger can be used to measure the temperature of a cooling object at intervals as it cools.

Take note however that every data logging system needs to be calibrated and checked to ensure its sensors give accurate and reliable measurements.

Data analysis packages do not need to be very sophisticated to assist you in making sense of your measurements. For example, pairs of measurements of two quantities can be fed into a program either directly or via a keyboard. The data can be presented on screen to see how one quantity affects the other, and the quantities can be manipulated to find out if there is a mathematical relationship between them. A 'least squares fit' program will plot a graph of two related variables to identify links between the two variables. For example, a graph of pressure against volume for a gas would show that the pressure of the gas goes down as the volume goes up. However, a graph of pressure against 1/volume would show exactly how the pressure is related to the volume since the pressure is proportional to 1/volume. A data analysis package usually has the facility to work out 1/volume from the volume data and plot the pressure against 1/volume with no more than a few key strokes.

Data bases can be used to hold revision information or to keep track of your revision schedule or to hold data on questions you have tackled during the course. Data bases are essentially lists so could also be used to list properties of materials such as melting points, boiling points etc.

Charts, graphs and tables can be used to display graphs and tables of measured data from data loggers or to display charts, graphs and tables of data from data bases or spread sheets. The use of data analysis packages is mentioned earlier. Data can be extracted from a spread sheet and presented in various forms, including bar charts, pie charts and line graphs.

Spreadsheets in physics can be used to provide a numerical solution to any equation involving a quantity which changes. For example, the coordinates of a projectile launched with a certain initial velocity can be calculated at successive times using a spread sheet, as shown in Fig 8.1 opposite.

> Insert the formula $X = Ut = 5t$ into the $t = 1$ X-column box and the formula $Y = \frac{1}{2}gt^2$ into the $t = 1$ Y-column box using an indexed reference to the box $t = 1$. Then copy down each column to obtain the data as shown in Fig 8.1.

The data can be easily extracted into a graph if required as shown in Fig 8.2 opposite.

Word processing is a useful skill to acquire when it comes to drafting laboratory reports for preliminary checking since changes can easily be made after you have read your report through for the first time. Charts, graphs and tables can easily be inserted into word processed reports. However, don't be fooled into imagining high-quality presentation is a substitute for high-quality content.

Internet and e-mail are useful communication tools to find information and to seek help from experts. A clear aim and a definite address are essential to gain information off the Internet quickly, otherwise you can waste valuable time. Don't expect same-day replies using e-mail as scientists are busy people.

Initial horizontal speed = 5m/s		
Initial vertical speed = 0		
Time t/s	Y / m	X / m
0	0	0
1	4.9	5
2	19.6	10
3	44.1	15
4	78.4	20
5	122.5	25

Fig 8.1 Spreadsheet example

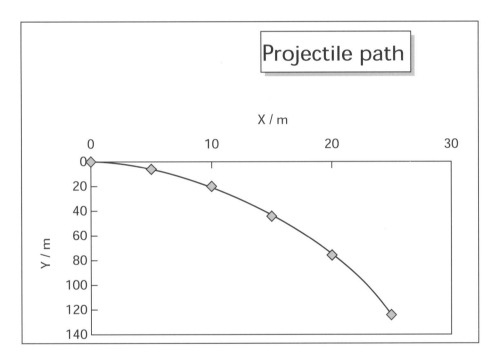

Fig 8.2 Graph produced from spreadsheet data

Revision should be a continual process throughout your course. As examinations approach, revision practice of past papers becomes more and more important. Physics examinations test candidates in a variety of ways:

- Factual recall
- Understanding ideas
- Laboratory skills
- Comprehension and writing skills
- Powers of organisation
- Mathematical skills
- Data analysis skills

Each awarding body with its particular syllabus or subject specification tests your knowledge and skills with its own distinct range of papers. All awarding bodies are required to include a specified core of essential knowledge and understanding at AS level and at Advanced level. Syllabuses and subject specifications vary outside these core topics, all non-core material being compulsory in specifications which do not include optional topics. Whichever specification you are following, your final grade is based on your performance in written papers (which usually count for at least 80% of the total mark) and on your standard of practical work, assessed either through course-work or through a practical examination. At Advanced level, your mark on written papers will be based on module tests taken during the course or at the end of the course as well as a 'synoptic' test at the end of the course. The mark for each section of a question is always indicated at the end of a section and this is a guide to the time you should spend on each section of a question. For example, if a 90 minute paper carries 60 marks, then you should expect to spend about 15 minutes on a question that carries 10 marks. Clearly, it is important to work through past papers to famil-iarise yourself with the demands of the paper in terms of time as well as in terms of the expected standard. Published mark schemes of recent past papers are available from most awarding bodies.

Module tests

Module tests usually consist of compulsory ques-tions, generally composed of several short ques-tions and one or two longer questions. Multiple choice questions may also be used for some modules by some awarding bodies. You should ensure you know exactly what type of questions you will face on each module test as the question types are likely to differ from module to module and from one awarding body to another.

Each module test is based on a limited section of the specification which enables your revision to be focused. However, if taken during the course, you will probably not have much time for revision so you must keep on top of the work, topic by topic. Early entry to module tests is not really advisable in physics as your skills do develop considerably during the course.

Objective (i.e. multiple choice) questions require fast recall and understanding of basic ideas across all topics in the module. Questions can be search-ing but you must not spend too long on any one. Work through the full set of multiple choice ques-tions in order; if a question takes more than its fair share of time, abandon it and return to it later. When you have worked through the set in this way, return to the questions you couldn't manage first time. If necessary, make an educated guess from the alternatives you think may be correct.

Short questions on module tests or on the compul-sory sections of end-of-course papers are likely to test factual recall and understanding of key ideas. A short question may probe your grasp of part of a longer proof or your ability to use an equation or to describe key concepts. An example is given below.

> *Question*
> *(a) Write down an equation linking the pressure of an ideal gas to its density and the r.m.s. speed of its molecules.*
> *(b) Explain why the Earth is able to retain an atmosphere whereas the Moon cannot.*

Clearly, your answer to (b) requires an understand-ing that molecules have a range of speeds and that the mean square speed is proportional to the absolute temperature. You need to link these ideas up with ideas about escape velocity to explain why gas molecules released on the lunar surface escape into space.

Longer questions can appear on module tests as compulsory questions or in a section of an end-of-course paper which might offer a choice of ques-tions. Detailed proofs or questions about experiments or demonstrations are likely topics for long questions. Another source is your ability to link topics together and to use basic principles in situations you have not met before. Longer ques-tions which are structured require little planning as you are expected to answer the question part-by-part. At the other extreme, you could be expected to provide a 30 minute answer of a question consist-ing of a few lines only, perhaps based on a detailed proof or an experiment. Clearly, planning is vital before you begin your written answer.

Option topics vary between awarding bodies. The questions are usually compulsory and structured, designed to probe in-depth knowledge and understanding. Option questions may draw on core topics where appropriate.

Synoptic assessment

Synoptic papers are taken at the end of an Advanced level course as they are intended to test knowledge and skills which link topics together. All Advanced level specifications now include a minimum of 20% synoptic assessment. Depending on the awarding body, a synoptic paper might consist of:

1. data analysis questions, or
2. a comprehension paper, or
3. short or long questions based on topics that link content from different modules together, or
4. practical work that builds on knowledge and skills from across the specification.

Data analysis questions are set by some awarding bodies in distinct sections or papers. However, analysing data can be a feature of longer questions, comprehension papers and practical examinations. In addition, data analysis is a key part of experimental physics so is needed for practicals and projects. Examination questions that test data analysis skills directly supply experimental measurements, usually with brief details of how the measurements were obtained. You are then expected to analyse the data and establish links between the physical variables involved. In this situation, it may be helpful to recall similar techniques you have used during your course. For example, you may have used log–log graphs (see p. 28) to establish the link between the current and the p.d. across a light bulb. If you are asked in an examination question to plot a log–log graph in an entirely different topic, your previous work gives you the general idea. Data analysis skills need to be developed throughout your course; often, such skills are not taught formally so you may find *Chapter 5 in this Course Study Guide* helpful.

Comprehension papers often present basic principles in situations that you would not otherwise meet on your syllabus. You are expected to recognise the basic principles and apply them to the situation. Obviously comprehension and writing skills are under test; but so too is your grasp of basic ideas and factual recall. (Comprehension skills are discussed in more detail on pp. 56–57).

Short or long questions used for synoptic assessment link topics from later modules to topics from earlier modules to probe understanding of principles and concepts. In addition, synoptic assessment features questions that test understanding and knowledge through links between later topics.

EXAMPLES

1. (a) Calculate the resistivity of the material of a wire of length 800 mm and diameter 0.32 mm that had a resistance of 6.5 Ω.
   (b) The wire was stretched to increase its length to 850 mm. Assuming its volume did not change, calculate (i) its diameter, (ii) its resistance in the stretched condition.

Commentary *This question starts with basic electricity then links to ideas about volume without asking for a volume calculation. In (a) the calculation requires straightforward recall of resistivity calculations. In (b) you need to reuse the resistivity equation with new values of length and area of cross-section. To find the length, recall that the volume of a wire equals its length × its area of cross-section so that its new area of cross-section equals its initial area of cross-section × its initial length/its final length.*

Solution

a) Use the equation for resistivity $\rho = \dfrac{RA}{l}$

   where $A = \dfrac{\pi(0.32 \times 10^{-3})^2}{4} = 8.04 \times 10^{-8} \text{ m}^2$

   Hence $\rho = \dfrac{6.50 \times 8.04 \times 10^{-8}}{0.800} = 6.53 \times 10^{-7} \text{ } \Omega \text{ m}$

b) (i) Use volume = length × area of cross-section to calculate the new area of cross-section A' for length l'; hence $A' = \dfrac{A \times l}{l'} = \dfrac{0.800 \, A}{0.850} = 0.941 \, A$.

   $\therefore \dfrac{\pi d'^2}{4} = \dfrac{0.941 \pi d^2}{4}$, where d' and d are the new and initial diameters respectively.

   Hence $d' = (0.941)^{1/2} d = 0.970 \, d = 0.310$ mm

   (ii) New resistance

   $R' = \dfrac{\rho l'}{A'} = \dfrac{6.53 \times 10^{-7} \times 0.850}{0.941 \times 8.04 \times 10^{-8}} = 7.34 \text{ } \Omega$

2. a) A 100 μF capacitor was charged from a 9.0 V battery then discharged through a 47 kΩ resistor. Calculate:
   (i) the initial charge and energy stored in the capacitor,
   (ii) the time taken after the discharge process started for the capacitor to lose half of its initial charge.

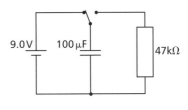

9.0 V   100 μF   47 kΩ

Fig 9.1

b) Capacitor discharge and radioactive decay are examples of exponential decrease processes. The radioactive decay constant λ for an unstable isotope $= \dfrac{\ln 2}{T_{1/2}}$, where $T_{1/2}$ is the half-life of the isotope. The time taken for a capacitor C to discharge through a resistor R to half its initial potential difference $= RC \ln 2$.

(i) Show that the unit of λ and the unit of $1/RC$ are both the same.

(ii) Calculate the time taken for the capacitor in (a) to lose 99% of its initial stored energy.

Commentary *This question starts with a capacitor discharge calculation in which the capacitor energy formula must also be brought in. Knowledge and skills about working out units from given equations is then probed. Finally, the link with radioactive decay as another exponential process is then probed to find out if the concept of half-life is properly understood. Beware though, as the final part of the question also requires very careful reading before setting pen to paper. Highlight the key words and numbers before you think about your approach to solving this part of the question.*

Solution

a) (i) $Q_0 = CV = 100~\mu F \times 9.0~V = 9.00 \times 10^{-4}~C$
   $E_0 = \frac{1}{2} CV^2 = 0.5 \times 50 \times 10^{-6} \times 9.0^2$
   $\qquad = 2.03 \times 10^{-3}~J$

   (ii) For $Q = 0.5~Q_0$, the capacitor discharge equation $Q = Q_0\, e^{-t/RC}$ gives $0.5~Q_0 = Q_0\, e^{-t/RC}$
   $\therefore 0.5 = e^{-t/RC}$ which gives $t = -RC \ln 0.5$
   $(= RC \ln 2) = 100~\mu F \times 47~k\Omega \times \ln 2 = 3.26~s$

b) (i) The unit of λ is the same as the unit of $1/\text{time}$ since $\lambda = \dfrac{\ln 2}{T_{1/2}}$. The unit of RC is the same as the unit of time since $RC \ln 2$ represents the 'half-life' of the discharge.
   Hence the unit of $1/RC$ is also the same as the unit of $1/\text{time}$.

   (ii) The loss of 99% of its inital energy corresponds to the stored energy falling to 1% of the initial stored energy. Hence the energy stored $E = 0.01~E_0$ thus $\frac{1}{2}CV^2 = 0.01 \times \frac{1}{2}~CV_0^2$.
   $\therefore V = (0.01)^{1/2}~V_0 = 0.10~V_0$ or $Q = 0.10~Q_0$
   The half-life of the process $= 3.26~s$ (as

worked out above)
If the discharge takes n half-lives,
$0.5^n = 0.1$ $\therefore n = 3.32$
$\therefore$ Time taken $= 3.32 \times 3.26 = 10.8~s$.

Practical skills

Practical skills are assessed either through coursework (internal assessment) or by means of a practical examination (external assessment).

Coursework may consist of several short practical experiments or a longer investigation or project. Awarding bodies take great care to ensure that the standards of internal assessment are the same from one school or college to another. After your coursework report is assessed by your teacher according to the awarding body's criteria, a selection of coursework from your school or college is sent to the awarding body where the standard of work is checked. You must adhere to your teacher's deadlines (which are set by the awarding body) for handing in coursework. Your organisational skills are important as well as your practical skills and your communication skills. See pp. 50–53 for more information on projects.

Practical examinations can either be in the form of a series of short experiments or a single much longer experiment. Short experiments test a particular technique or skill (using a vernier, for example) and usually require recall of basic knowledge. Some short experiments involve making and then explaining observations to test your understanding of basic ideas; usually, the instructions are set out in the question step-by-step, and you are expected to know how to use the instruments to carry out each step.

For the long experiment in a practical examination, planning and organisational skills are important. Knowledge of the correct techniques for making accurate measurements is expected. See Chapter 6. You also need to know how to reduce and to estimate errors, and the skills for analysing data are important. So too is the need to explain your methods clearly. Advice on writing up practicals is given in Chapter 7.

10 A-level grade criteria

The awarding bodies set the grade boundaries on each examination paper in accordance with grade criteria which are the same in any given subject for all examination boards. These grade criteria ensure that identical grades from each awarding body represent the same standard of work. The criteria also ensure that the grades each year are no harder and no easier to achieve than in previous years. The grade criteria statements for each grade boundary are set out below to help you do as well as you can in your examinations. The criteria have been rewritten in 'student-friendly' language.

Grade E	Grade C	Grade A
Knowledge and understanding Recall knowledge from parts of the course.	**Knowledge and understanding** Recall knowledge from most parts of the course.	**Knowledge and understanding** Recall and use knowledge from all parts of the course, with few significant omissions.
Select discrete items of knowledge to answer structured questions.	Select and make good use of information to solve problems, and demonstrate some knowledge of the links between different areas of the subject.	Select appropriate information to construct arguments or techniques to solve problems, and show understanding of the principles and concepts in all parts of the course.
Make some use of the terminology of the subject in answers.	Make some use of the terminology and concepts of the subject in answers.	Link different areas of the subject to solve appropriate problems, and demonstrate an understanding of the relationships between linked areas.
Demonstrate some understanding of fundamental principles and concepts.	Demonstrate significant understanding of the main principles and concepts.	
Application Apply knowledge and understanding to familiar contexts.	**Application** Apply knowledge and understanding to contexts which provide some guidance.	**Application** Apply knowledge and understanding of physical principles to familiar and unfamiliar contexts.
Carry out straightforward calculations with some guidance using the correct units for physical quantities.	Carry out familiar calculations correctly in most areas of physics, giving the correct units for most quantities. In carrying out calculations, show some understanding of the physical principles involved and magnitudes of common physical quantities.	Carry out extended calculations correctly with little or no guidance. In carrying out calculations, show good understanding of the links between the physical quantities involved.

Grade E	Grade C	Grade A
Experimental activities Plan some aspects of an experimental activity.	**Experimental activities** Plan an experimental activity clearly.	**Experimental activities** Identify and plan an experimental activity clearly and effectively, using knowledge and understanding of physics and use a range of relevant techniques with care and skill.
Make and record some appropriate measurements with care and appropriate procedure.	Make and record measurements with skill and care, showing awareness of the need for appropriate precision.	Make and record sufficient measurements with appropriate precision.
Present results as appropriate and describe their outcome.	Interpret an explain experimental results, making some use of mathematical techniques and fundamental principles of physics.	Interpret and explain experimental results, making sound use of fundamental principles of physics.
		Evaluate critically the reliability of chosen methods.

11 Key skills through Advanced level physics

What are key skills?

Whatever you go on to do, there are certain key skills you will need in work or in higher education or training. These include:

- communication skills
- information technology skills
- application of number skills
- improving your own learning and performance
- working with others
- problem solving.

It is now possible to gain a qualification in these skills while you are doing your post-16 study. This qualification will carry points towards university admission and be useful to show employers. Improving your skills will also help your study.

Key skills are assessed at three levels. Level 3 is the one that is appropriate to post-16 students. Assessment will be through moderated course-work evidence and an external test in each of the first three key skills listed. The suggestions below apply only to coursework. Some of the skills can be demonstrated through activities which occur in AS or A-level physics, in particular the first three key skills listed.

The skills you need to demonstrate for Level 3 of this qualification are given below. You should not expect to be able to demonstrate all the skills through any one subject. Some suggestions as to how you can develop and demonstrate key skills through your studies in physics are also given below.

Communication Level 3

C3.1a Contribute to a group discussion about a complex subject.

You are sure to have opportunities for discussion during your course, for example about the history and development of an idea or theory in physics or about the effect of some aspect of physics on the environment or about the economic and social aspects of physics.

You will need to show that you can:

- listen to what others have to say,
- be sensitive to the views and feelings of others,
- gather your thoughts before you speak and make clear and relevant contributions.

C3.1b Make a presentation about a complex subject, using at least one image to illustrate complex points.

Your teacher will almost certainly give you the chance to make a presentation to the class. This may be about a factual topic that you have researched or a more open-ended topic such as those mentioned in C3.1a.

You will need to show that you can:

- Speak clearly and adapt your presentation to suit the situation. It is a good idea to practice your presentation aloud to get the timing right and find someone to listen to you who is prepared to make helpful observations about whether you can be heard, and whether your content makes sense.
- Structure your arguments logically. (Make notes to keep yourself on track, but don't just read out a prepared script.)
- Use one or more images. These could be posters, handouts or overhead projector transparencies, possibly prepared using a computer presentation of graphics or a word processing package (thus hitting IT targets too). These will help to keep you on track. You might base your image on a photocopied or scanned image that you have amended in some way. but whatever you do make sure it is relevant and not just decorative.

C3.2 Read and synthesise information from *two* extended documents about a complex subject, one of these documents should include at least *one* image.

'Synthesise' means 'put together'. This target could be approached in a number of contexts – possibly while preparing a piece of written work (essay), a talk or in planning an experiment or investigation.

You will need to show that you can:

- Select relevant information from more than one source. (Use your textbook, popular science magazines, the Internet, e-mail, etc.)
- Put together relevant information in a suitable form for your purpose.
- Use and interpret visual information – for example a graph or diagram.

C3.3 Write *two* different types of document about complex subjects. One piece of writing should be an extended document and include at least *one* image.

These could be essays (e.g. an essay on materials or energy resources) or reports of experiments or investigations. You will need to decide the best style for each purpose. For example, practical instructions may best be presented as a series of numbered or bulleted points rather than as paragraphs or prose. Diagrams or other images will almost always be needed in a physics essay or a practical report. You will need to ensure your work is legible and your spelling, grammar and punctuation are accurate so your meaning is clear.

Information technology Level 3

You must plan and carry through at least one substantial activity that includes tasks for IT3.1, IT3.2 and IT3.3.

IT3.1 Plan and use different sources to search for and select information required for *two* different purposes.

Your purpose could be preparing for a discussion, preparing a talk, writing an essay, planning practical work.

Sources could include:

- General CD-ROMs such as *Encarta* or other encyclopedias; science CD-ROMs such as *New Scientist*. Find out what is available in your school or college library.
- The Internet. A few useful ideas for sites are given below or you could use a search engine. All sorts of topics can be accessed free including astronomy sites and data sources on material and energy resources. There is so much information that you will need to restrict your searching. Remember also that some sites will be more reliable than others – one run by a university physics department or the Institute of Physics (IOP) or PPARC, the Particle Physics and Astronomy Research Council, is more likely to be accurate than an unknown site. Sites run by nuclear energy companies are less likely to highlight radioactive waste problems while environmental watchdog sites would highlight such problems. You need to exercise judgement!

IT3.2 Explore, develop and exchange information and derive new information required for *two* different purposes.

This could include the use of a spreadsheet or other data-handling package to process the results of some experimental work. If your school or college has an intranet, you could share your results with the rest of your group using e-mail.

IT3.3 Present information from different sources for *two* different purposes and audiences. This work must include at least *one* example of text, *one* example of images and *one* example of numbers.

You could produce a practical write-up using a word-processor. Your report could include diagrams from a graphics package, results which have been processed using a spreadsheet and charts or graphs drawn from the data in the spreadsheet.

Application of number Level 3

You must plan and carry through at least one substantial and complex activity that includes tasks for N3.1, N3.2 and N3.3.

N3.1 Plan, interpret information from *two* different types of source, including a large data set.

This could relate to the planning of practical work and treatment and calculation of results – using paper and pencil, calculator or computer (for example a spreadsheet). If you take results from the whole of your teaching group, you could assemble a large data set. You could compare your result for, say, the resistance per unit length of a wire with those of the rest of the class, each group using wires of the same material but of differing diameters, to give a large data set which you then use to determine the resistivity of the material of the wire. The result can then be compared with the accepted result in a data book.

N3.2 Carry out multi-stage calculations to do with:

a) amounts and sizes;
b) scales and proportion;
c) handling statistics;
d) rearranging and using formulae.

Evidence should include working with a large data set on at least one occasion.

You will find plenty of opportunities for these skills when dealing with calculation questions or with practical results. Most quantitative work will involve rearranging formulae and carrying out calculations involving numbers in standard form. In addition, the topics you study will range from the smallest possible scale to astronomical scales. Proportionality occurs in many practical situations where a link is to be sought or confirmed between physical quantities. Calculating averages is a simple statisical exercise, for example measuring the diameter of a wire at several positions then working out the mean diameter of the wire. Plotting and using lines of best fit is another statistical exercise.

N3.3 Interpret results of your calculations, present your findings and justify your methods. You must use at least *one* graph, *one* chart and *one* diagram.

You can demonstrate these skills through practical reports which involve making measurements and analysing and evaluating them. For example, a report on an investigation of the deflection of beta particles by a magnetic field would involve diagrams of the practical arrangement, a chart of the magnetic field pattern, a table of the measurements and a graph of the results to show the results with and without the magnetic field present. Your report would need to include a section on why you chose the method you followed, giving information about preliminary tests or other factors that guided your choices.

Most of the key skills occur at least once at some stage in your AS or A-level physics course so you don't have to do much beyond your usual physics studies to demonstrate these skills. Remember that some of the skills can be demonstrated through your other subjects. You don't need to demonstrate everything in every one of your subjects. However, you need to collect the evidence that you have demonstrated these skills and your teachers need to verify your evidence. You will probably need to collate your evidence in a folder and fill a few forms in – nothing too painful if you are methodical. Physicists are very versatile because most of the key skills are part and parcel of the everyday activities of a physicist. For example, some A-level physics activities that take in most of the above skills are:

1. Essay on a chosen topic (e.g. an aspect of materials or on energy resources); C3.1a, C3.1b, C3.2, C3.3, IT3.1, IT3.2, IT3.3
2. Practical investigation (e.g. resistivity, deflection of beta particles by a magnetic field, measurement of *g*); C3.3, IT3.1, IT3.2, IT3.3, N3.1, N3.2, N3.3

Summary

C3.1a Contribute to a group discussion about a complex subject

C3.1b Make a presentation about a complex subject, using at least one image to illustrate complex points.

C3.2 Read and synthesise information from **two** extended documents about a complex subject, one of these documents should include at least **one** image.

C3.3 Write **two** different types of document about complex subjects. One piece of writing should be an extended document and include at least **one** image.

IT3.1 Plan and use different sources to search for and select information required for **two** different purposes.

IT3.2 Explore, develop and exchange information and derive new information to meet **two** different purposes.

IT3.3 Present information from different sources for **two** different purposes and audiences. This work must include **one** example of text, **one** example of images and **one** example of numbers.

N3.1 Plan and interpret information from **two** different types of source, including a large data set.

N3.2 Carry out multi-stage calculations to do with: a) amounts and sizes, b) scales and proportion; c) handling statistics; d) rearranging and using formulae.
Evidence should include working with a large data set on at least **one** occasion.

N3.3 Interpret the results of your calculations, present your findings and justify your methods. You must use at least **one** graph, **one** chart and **one** diagram.

Answers

Chapter 2 p. 9

1. a) **E** b) **B** c) **C** d) **E**
2. a) 54.4 g   b) 123.4 g   c) 107 cm^3
   d) Density = 1150 kg m^{-3}
3. a) 0.230 m   b) 3.25 × 10^{-3} m^2
   c) 8.15 × 10^{-6} m^3 d) 7360 kg m^{-3}
4. a) Volume = $\pi r^2 L = \pi \times (0.026)^2 \times 0.2$
   $\qquad\qquad = 4.25 \times 10^{-4}$ m^3.
   b) Mass = volume × density
   $\qquad\qquad = 4.25 \times 10^{-4} \times 2700 = 1.14$ kg.
5. a) Radius r = 6 mm = 6.0 × 10^{-3} m,
   Volume $V = \frac{4}{3}\pi r^3 = \frac{4}{3}\pi \times (0.006)^3$
   $\qquad\qquad = 9.0 \times 10^{-7}$ m^3
   b) Rearranging the above equation gives

$$r^3 = \frac{3V}{4\pi} = \frac{3 \times 4.80 \times 10^{-6}}{4\pi}$$

$$= 1.14 \times 10^{-6} \text{ m}^3$$

   Hence $r = (1.14 \times 10^{-6})^{1/3} = 1.05 \times 10^{-2}$ m
   $\qquad\qquad = 10.5$ mm
   Therefore diameter = 21.0 mm.

Chapter 4, p. 36

1. a) 2.045 × 10^8 b) 2.376 × 10^{-2}
   c) 1.463 × 10^{19} d) 1.457 × 10^{-5}
   e) 3.807 × 10^{21} f) 21.91
   g) 1.325 × 10^{13} h) 1.01 × 10^{-2}
   i) 1.286 × 10^{11} j) 3.627 × 10^{-3}
2. a) 5.720   b) 1.051 × 10^2 c) 6.857
   d) 386.2   e) 81.20   f) 0.446
   g) 4.862 × 10^6 h) 1.165   i) 156.3
   j) 8.025

4. a) −1, 4   b) $y = -4x$
5. a) $y = -x + 5$, 5   b) 3.54
6. a) $x = 1, y = 3$ b) $a = 2.4, b = -0.4$
   c) $p = 2, q = 4$ d) $x = 3, y = 1$ e) $u = 1$,
   $v = 5$ and $u = 5, v = 1$
7. a) f^2 b) ln I c) $1/r^2$ d) p
   e) ln $(C - C_0)$
8. a) A   b) C   c) B   d) E   e) D
9. a) $6x$ b) $2 - 2x$ c) $-6/x^3$ d) $-3Ae^{-3x}$
   e) $2 \cos 2x$
10. a) flux linkage   b) charge   c) work
    d) energy per unit volume   e) velocity
11. a) $A = 100, \mu = 0.204$ b)(i) 81.5
    (ii) 13.0   c)(i) 3.40 (ii) 11.29
12. a) 0.139   b) 2

Chapter 5, p. 44

1. a) kg m s^{-1} b) kg m^3 s^{-3} A^{-2}
   c) kg m s^{-3} K^{-1} d) kg m^{-3}
   e) A^2 s^4 m^{-3} kg^{-1}
3. a) 0.28%, 0.33%   b) 7690 kg m^{-3}
   c) 1.3%
4. a) 0.3%, 0.6%   b) 9.76 m s^{-2}
   c) 0.15 m s^{-2}
6. b) 2.5   c)(i) 0.27, 0.48, 0.69,
   0.91 kN sm^{-1} (ii) 0.053 kN s m^{-1},
   10.7 N s^2 m^{-2}
7. 27.2 min: $k = 2.36 \times 10^{-4}$ mm^{-1},
   $x = 18.5$ mm; gradient = −2
8. b) $\alpha = 1.34 \times 10^{-3}$ K^{-1}, $\beta = 3.75 \times 10^{-6}$ K^{-2}
   c) 27 d)(i) 1505, 1535 K (ii) 8.6, 14.3 mA